Guidance notes for the

Engineering and Construction Contract

This contract should be used for the appointment of a contractor for engineering and construction work, including any level of design responsibility

Wardell Armstrong LLP

Sir Henry Doulton House
Forge Lane, Etruria
Stoke on Trent
ST1 5NN
Tel: 0845 111 7777
Fax: 0845 111 8888

An NEC document

June 2005
(with amendments June 2006)

NEC is a division of Thomas Telford Ltd, which is a wholly owned subsidiary of the Institution of Civil Engineers (ICE), the owner and developer of the NEC.

The NEC is a family of standard contracts, each of which has these characteristics:

- Its use stimulates good management of the relationship between the two parties to the contract and, hence, of the work included in the contract.

- It can be used in a wide variety of commercial situations, for a wide variety of types of work and in any location.

- It is a clear and simple document – using language and a structure which are straightforward and easily understood.

This document comprises the guidance notes for the NEC Engineering and Construction Contract.

ISBN (complete box set) 0 7277 3382 6
ISBN (this document) 0 7277 3366 4
ISBN (Engineering and Construction Contract) 0 7277 3359 1
ISBN (Engineering and Construction Contract Flow Charts) 0 7277 3367 2

Consultative edition 1991
First edition 1993
Second edition November 1995
Third edition June 2005
Reprinted with amendments June 2006

Cover photo, Golden Jubilee Bridge, courtesy of City of Westminster

9 8 7 6 5 4 3

British Library Cataloguing in Publication Data for this publication is available from the British Library.

Typeset by Academic + Technical, Bristol

Printed and bound in Great Britain by Bell & Bain Limited, Glasgow, UK

CONTENTS

ACKNOWLEDGEMENTS

For the third edition of the NEC Engineering and Construction Contract these Guidance Notes were produced by the Institution of Civil Engineers and were mainly drafted by Peter Cousins, Colin Reed and Tom Nicholson with the assistance of members of the NEC Panel.

The original NEC was designed and drafted by Dr Martin Barnes then of Coopers and Lybrand with the assistance of Professor J. G. Perry then of The University of Birmingham, T. W. Weddell then of Travers Morgan Management, T. H. Nicholson, Consultant to the Institution of Civil Engineers, A. Norman then of the University of Manchester Institute of Science and Technology and P. A. Baird, then Corporate Contracts Consultant, Eskom, South Africa.

The members of the NEC Panel are:

P. Higgins, BSc, CEng, FICE, FCIArb (Chairman)
P. A. Baird, BSc, CEng, FICE, M(SA)ICE, MAPM
M. Barnes, BSc(Eng), PhD, FREng, FICE, FCIOB, CCMI, ACIArb, MBCS, FInstCES, FAPM
A. J. Bates, FRICS, MInstCES
A. J. M. Blackler, BA, LLB(Cantab), MCIArb
P. T. Cousins, BEng(Tech), DipArb, CEng, MICE, MCIArb, MCMI
L. T. Eames, BSc, FRICS, FCIOB
F. Forward, BA(Hons), DipArch, MSc(Const Law), RIBA, FCIArb
Professor J. G. Perry, MEng, PhD, CEng, FICE, MAPM
N. C. Shaw, FCIPS, CEng, MIMechE
T. W. Weddell, BSc, CEng, DIC, FICE, FIStructE, ACIArb

NEC Consultant:

R. A. Gerrard, BSc(Hons), MRICS, FCIArb, FInstCES

Secretariat:

A. Cole, LLB, LLM, BL
J. M. Hawkins, BA(Hons), MSc
F. N. Vernon (Technical Adviser), BSc, CEng, MICE

AMENDMENTS JUNE 2006

The following amendments have been made since the June 2005 edition.

Page	Clause	Line
34	14	Last paragraph deleted: 'An example of a Risk Register layout is given on page 35'
48	32.1	4 deleted: 'and of notified early warning matters'
68	60	15 'Part one of the Contract Data also permits' replaced with 'Option Z may be used by'
136	53 53	1 'D' replaced with 'C' 3 'C' replaced with 'D'
139	Format X15 X16 X18	blank columns 3 & 4 deleted 4 in row below W2, sub-heading 'Secondary' inserted last column 'A, B, C, D, E' replaced with 'A to F' last column 'A to F' replaced with 'A to E' in row below X18, option 'X19 – Not used in ECC' inserted
143	Appendix 4	21 'Equipment,' inserted after 'people'
144	Various	example amended to include assessment of Equipment
146	Worked example, 1	4 Added '(with amendments June 2006)'
149	Worked example 7 Worked example	Deleted 'If there are additional compensation events', following 4 lines and comment box Share percentage example – amounts changed

FOREWORD

'A Fundamental Review'

In September 1985 the Council of the Institution of Civil Engineers approved a recommendation from its Legal Affairs Committee 'to lead a fundamental review of alternative contract strategies for civil engineering design and construction with the objective of identifying the needs for good practice'. Preparation of a specification of a new style contract was commissioned in July 1986. The work was carried out by Dr Martin Barnes, then of Martin Barnes Project Management with the assistance of Dr John Perry, then of the Project Management Group at the University of Manchester Institute of Science and Technology.

The specification was submitted to the Legal Affairs Committee in December 1986 and, after modification, presented to a limited audience in September 1987. In June 1988 the Council decided to develop a draft of the new style contract through a working group of members of the Institution, representatives of contractors, consulting engineers and employers. The drafting team was led by Dr Martin Barnes.

Consultation

A consultative version of the New Engineering Contract (NEC) was published in January 1991. Comments were received from a large number of organisations and individuals including employers, contractors, consulting engineers, surveyors and lawyers. Discussion also took place at seminars and conferences and with various organisations.

The consultative version of the NEC was used in a number of different types of contract in various countries including the United Kingdom, South Africa, Hong Kong and Belize. Valuable feedback was received. A first edition of the NEC was published in March 1993.

Latham – 'Constructing the Team'

In July 1994, Sir Michael Latham produced his report 'Constructing the Team'. This report was commissioned by the UK Government in collaboration with the construction industry and its professions. It recommended that the NEC should be adopted by clients in both the private and public sectors and suggested that it should become a national standard contract across the whole of engineering and construction work generally.

Following the publication of the Latham Report, the Institution of Civil Engineers decided to bring forward the publication of a second edition of the NEC. The second edition included a large number of small refinements to the first edition prompted by further comment on the first edition and by feedback from projects on which the first edition had been used. Extensive changes were made to the insurance and adjudication provisions. It also included the changes recommended in the Latham Report in order that it would comply with the principles for a modern contract set out in the report and that it should be entirely appropriate for wide use.

One of the recommendations in the Latham Report was that the name of the document should be changed. This is why, in the second edition, the name of the main contract was changed to Engineering and Construction Contract (ECC).

The third edition

Since the introduction of the second edition, the ECC has become widely used by employers, contractors and consultants wishing to embrace the principles of partnering envisaged in 'Constructing the Team'. The third edition of this contract should be seen as an evolutionary rather than revolutionary change to the second edition. Its purpose is twofold.

Firstly it aims to continue the process of improvement and refinement prompted by feedback from those who it is aimed for, i.e. the many people who use it to manage projects, large and small. In doing so the purpose has been to simplify the contract wherever possible and remove, or solve, some of the problems that its use can cause in practice.

Secondly it aims to update the contract to embrace project management tools such as risk registers or partnering, increasingly being demanded by clients and their advisers.

The NEC family of contracts

The first edition of the ECC, then called the NEC, started life as a single contract between a client and a contractor for the management of individual projects. With the development of further contracts for different relationships it is now one of many contracts in the NEC family of contracts. Other contracts include:

- NEC Professional Services Contract
- NEC Engineering and Construction Short Contract
- NEC Engineering and Construction Subcontract
- NEC Engineering and Construction Short Subcontract
- NEC Term Service Contract
- NEC Framework Contract
- NEC Adjudicator's Contract

All of these follow the same basic principles and format as the original NEC. They can be used individually or together to cover all contractual relationships in the engineering, construction and building industries.

INTRODUCTION

Background

The NEC Engineering and Construction Contract (ECC) (previously the New Engineering Contract) has been developed to meet the current and future needs for a form of contract to be used in the engineering, building and construction industries. It is an improvement on existing standard contracts in a number of ways.

Purpose of guidance notes

The purpose of these guidance notes is to explain the background to the ECC, the reasons for some of its provisions and to provide guidance on how to use it.

Neither these guidance notes nor the flow charts published with the contract are contract documents, nor are they part of the ECC. They should not be used for legal interpretation of the meaning of the ECC.

The convention of using italics for terms which are identified in the Contract Data of the ECC and capital initials for terms defined in the ECC has been used in these guidance notes.

Objectives

The objectives for the design of the New Engineering Contract (NEC) contracts were to make improvements to more traditional forms of contract under three main headings.

Flexibility   The ECC is designed to be as flexible as possible. It can be used

- for engineering and construction work containing any or all of the traditional disciplines such as civil, electrical, mechanical and building work,
- whether the *Contractor* has full design responsibility, some design responsibility or no design responsibility,
- to provide all the current options for types of contract such as competitive tender (where the *Contractor* is committed to his offered prices), target contracts, cost reimbursable contracts and management contracts and
- in the United Kingdom and in other countries.

All the commonly used standard conditions of contract from the various sectors of engineering and construction were reviewed in the course of designing the ECC. Some of their provisions that were peculiar to particular sectors have been omitted where they are better included in the Works Information. Where they are essential, they have been included in the ECC itself. For example, the need to make full provision for off-site manufacture and testing of work which is characteristic of mechanical and electrical contracts has been included in the ECC.

In order to achieve uniformity across the various engineering, construction and building sectors, some changes of terminology from those normally used have been necessary. One example is that the word 'Equipment' is used for what, in the building and civil engineering sectors, has in the past been called 'Constructional Plant'. The word 'Plant' is used in the ECC as it is customarily used in all the other engineering sectors. The traditional civil engineering and building term 'temporary works' is covered by 'Equipment' as defined in ECC Clause 11.2(7) and therefore is not used.

Clarity and simplicity

Although a legal document, the ECC is written in ordinary language. As far as possible, it uses only words which are in common use. This makes it easier to understand by people who are not used to using formal contracts and by people whose first language is not English. It also makes it easier to translate into other languages. However, in the areas of insurance, disputes and termination, some phrases or terms which have a specific legal meaning have been retained.

As further aids to simplicity and clarity, a great deal of effort has been taken to reduce the content of the contract conditions to the minimum needed. This has resulted in the following.

- The number of clauses used and the amount of text in each are less than in many standard forms.
- Sentences are kept as short as possible.
- Sentences have been subdivided using bullet points to make them easier to understand.
- The various Option clauses are designed so that they only add to the core clauses rather than alter or delete them.
- The ECC neither requires nor contains cross-references between clauses.

To a person used to using more traditional forms of contract, the simplicity and clarity of the ECC may not be immediately apparent. This is because it uses words and grammar that, although common in everyday speech and writing, are not usually found in formal contract documents or other legal papers. The contract also uses a number of newly defined expressions that the more experienced reader may not be familiar with.

The ECC is arranged and organised in a structure which helps the user to gain familiarity with its contents. More importantly, the actions by the parties which follow from use of the ECC are defined precisely so that there should be few disputes about who is to do what and how.

The design of the ECC is based upon flow charts of the procedures to be followed by the parties named in the contract. One of the benefits of this approach to drafting has been that opportunities could be taken for simplifying the structure of the contract as well as ensuring that the procedures were not open-ended or conflicting. For example, almost all circumstances which may give rise to additional payment to the *Contractor* are identified as compensation events. The procedure for dealing with these events is mainly set out in the core clauses and includes review of both the cost and time implications. This contrasts with traditional forms of contract in which the procedure for compensation is different depending upon the nature of each event.

A fundamental objective of the ECC is that its use should minimise the incidence of disputes. Thus words like 'fair', 'reasonable' and 'opinion' have been used as little as possible. This does not mean that the flexibility of administering the contract has been reduced. For example, in most instances where the *Project Manager* is required to decide whether or not to accept a submission from the *Contractor*, reasons are given in the contract for a decision not to accept.

The *Project Manager* may still decide to reject the submission for some other reason, but in that case the *Contractor* may be entitled to compensation. This will significantly reduce uncertainty about the outcome of the contract. This benefits the *Contractor* without constraining the freedom of action of the *Project Manager* acting on behalf of the *Employer*.

Stimulus to good management

This is perhaps the most important characteristic of the ECC. Every procedure has been designed so that its implementation should contribute to, rather than detract from, the effectiveness of management of the work. This aspect of ECC is founded upon the proposition that foresighted, co-operative management of the interactions between the parties can reduce the risks inherent in construction and engineering work. Developments in project management techniques and their implementation over the past 20 years have moved faster than the evolution of forms of contract. With the ECC, it is now possible to build arrangements for the different parties to contribute to the management of a project upon improved practices and to motivate all parties, by means of the contract, to apply such practices to their work.

The ECC is therefore intended to provide a modern method for employers, designers, contractors and project managers to work collaboratively. It also enables them to achieve their own objectives more consistently than has been possible using more traditional forms of contract. Use of the ECC is intended to lead to a much reduced risk to the *Employer* of cost and time overruns and of poor performance of the completed projects. It should also lead to a much increased likelihood of achieving a profit for the *Contractor* and his subcontractors and suppliers.

The two principles on which the ECC is based and which impact upon the objective of stimulating good management are:

- foresight applied collboratively mitigates problems and shrinks risk, and
- clear division of function and responsibility helps accountability and motivates people to play their part.

A secondary but important theme is that people will be motivated to play their part in collaborative management if it is in their commercial and professional interest to do so. Reliance need not be placed upon exhortation, either within the contract or outside it.

Inevitably on any construction or engineering project there will be uncertainty and risks involved in carrying out the *works*. The ECC allocates the risks between the Parties clearly and simply. But it also helps to reduce the likelihood of those risks occurring and their subsequent impact, if they do occur, by the application of collaborative foresight and risk reduction procedures. In this way, it aims to improve the outcome of projects generally for parties whose interests might seem to be opposed.

A prominent example of the way that the procedures in the ECC are designed to stimulate good management is the early warning procedure. This is designed to ensure that the Parties are made aware as soon as possible of any event which may

- increase the amount that the *Employer* has to pay,
- delay Completion of the *works*,
- impair the performance of the *works,* once completed, or
- affect others working on the project.

The Parties are then required to meet, to seek mutually beneficial solutions to overcome these problems, and to operate a formal Risk Register of notified events.

A further example is the management of compensation events. These are events which are at the risk of the *Employer*, and which may lead to the payment to the *Contractor* changing or the Completion Date, i.e. the date by which the Contractor is required to complete the *works*, being extended. A principle of the ECC is that, when such an event occurs, the *Project Manager*, acting on behalf of the *Employer* and in communication with him, should, whenever possible, be presented with options for dealing with the problem from which he can choose, directed by the interests of the *Employer*.

The ECC is designed to ensure that the *Contractor* will be unaffected financially by the choice that the *Project Manager* makes. To achieve this, the *Contractor* prepares a quotation for the valuation of compensation events that is based upon a forecast of the impact which the change or problem will have upon his cost of carrying out the work – as forecast by him at the time the event is assessed. Where, as is often the case, alternative ways of dealing with the problem are possible, the *Contractor* prepares quotations for different ways of tackling the problem. The *Project Manager* selects one on the basis of which will best serve the interests of the *Employer*. Criteria for such selection can include lowest cost, least delay or best finished quality, or any combination of these.

In Options A and B the change to the amount that the *Contractor* is paid for the work is based on the quotation. The *Contractor* carries the potential risk or reward if his forecast of the cost impact is wrong, and the *Employer* has a firm commitment. The *Contractor*'s risk or reward is conceptually similar to the risk he takes when pricing a tender, but he will have better information on which to base his estimate. In Options C and D the quotation is used to vary the target, and so the Parties will share the risk and reward under the share mechanism.

This arrangement is intended to

- stimulate foresight,
- enable the *Employer* to make rational decisions about changes to the work with reasonable certainty of their cost and time implications, and
- put a risk on the *Contractor* which is tolerable and which motivates him to manage the new situation efficiently.

An important by-product is that few issues relating to valuation of the work or extensions of time are left to be settled after the event.

This approach has pervaded the drafting of the ECC and is the basis for most of the procedures which it contains. In designing the ECC, the motivation of each party in each action he is to take has been considered against good management criteria. Because this is motivation-driven, it does not appear in the words of the ECC itself but it is intended to result directly from the way in which the procedures are operated.

A typical aspect of this characteristic is the way in which the ECC makes use of the programme for design, construction and installation. Many of the detailed procedures rely upon the fact that an up-to-date and realistic programme maintained by the *Contractor* is used in joint decision-making between him and the *Project Manager*. The use of the programme is defined in some detail and in such a way that, again, the *Contractor* is motivated to keep it up-to-date and realistic. He is not simply exhorted to do so but rather it is in his, and the *Employer*'s, best interests to do so.

Subcontracts

The ECC has been designed on the assumption that work may be sub-contracted. The NEC family of contacts includes several contracts that can be used for this subcontracting. They are:

- the Engineering and Construction Subcontract (ECS),
- the Engineering and Construction Short Subcontract (ECSS), and
- the Professional Services Contract (PSC).

These are all based upon similar principles to the ECC and use common names and definitions. They have a small number of different provisions designed specifically for the different circumstances for which they should be used.

Users of the ECC who will become involved in the setting up of subcontracts are advised to read the guidance notes for the various forms before deciding which they should use.

Use of the same text in the main contract and the subcontract provides some back-to-back protection for main contractors using one of the NEC family. It also has the convenience that *Contractors'* and Subcontractors' staff do not have to become familiar with two different sets of text and procedure. There is nothing to prevent a subcontract using a different Option from that used in the main contract. An obvious example of this is where the main contract uses a cost reimbursable or target Option (C, D or E) whilst the subcontract uses a priced Option (A or B). Option F (management contract) has not been included in the ECS.

Some other changes

Two other specific changes from conventional construction practice deserve mention.

Firstly, subcontractors cannot be nominated. This change is made in order to simplify contract arrangements and to eliminate the clouding of responsibilities which nomination causes. Elimination of this clouding should not only reduce disputes but also strengthen the motivation of the parties to manage their activities. An *Employer* who has reasons for using a particular contractor for part of the works can use the ECC for a direct contract alongside other contractors. The effective use of Key Dates in the individual contracts will assist in the management of these different contractors.

Secondly, the financial control document in the ECC can be either a traditional bill of quantities or an activity schedule. An activity schedule is a list of items with lump sum prices. The total price for the work to be done is divided between each of the items. This is a simpler document to prepare and use than the traditional bill of quantities. The bill of quantities will normally be produced by or on behalf of the *Employer* and priced and extended by the tenderers. The activity schedule will normally be produced and priced by each of the tenderers. Therefore the use of an *activity schedule* rather than a *bill of quantities* will result in a decrease of the tender preparation time and costs for the *Employer* but an increase for that of all of the tenderers.

Application of the ECC

Although, at first reading, the ECC may appear to be similar in concept, if not in language, to existing standard forms, to rely upon such an impression would be wrong. In many ways it is radically different. As the flow charts show, most procedures are based on good management practice and often differ from current practice in some engineering and building disciplines. This is not change for the sake of change, little conventional practice remains when the principles of the ECC are applied.

The user of the ECC must, therefore, study it carefully, as the words are not simply different expressions of familiar practice.

The ECC is drafted in a simple and clear style, but its differences from current practice mean that some explanation and consideration of how it will work is necessary when it is first used. These guidance notes are essential reading for people using the ECC for the first time. They will continue to be useful in training people coming into the management of projects in how to make best use of the ECC as part of the NEC System. The published flow charts should also be referred to as illustrations of the procedures on which the ECC is based.

The published documents

Arrangement of the ECC

The ECC includes the following sections of text

- the core clauses,
- the main Option clauses,
- the dispute resolution Option clauses,
- the secondary Option clauses,
- the Schedule of Cost Components, and
- the Contract Data formats.

Other documents included in a contract when using the ECC will include

- the Works Information
- the Site Information, and
- documents resulting from choosing secondary Options, such as Performance Bond (if submitted before the Contract Date).

The successful tenderer's tender programme may also be incorporated as the Accepted Programme by reference in the Contract Data part two.

Depending on the choice of main Option, the documents may also include:

- an *activity schedule* or
- a *bill of quantities*.

The Schedule of Cost Components (SCC) or the Shorter SSCC is used, depending upon which main Option is chosen, to define those components of the Contractor's costs which are included in Defined Cost for all main Options except Option F.

Defined Cost is used to assess payments to the Contractor in Options C, D and E, and for assessing the cost effects of compensation events whichever main Option (except Option F) has been chosen.

The Contract Data are selected and completed for each contract. These data identify such things as the completion dates, the contract-specific documents (such as the Works Information – called the specification and drawings in other traditional contracts), interest rates and price adjustment indices to be used.

The following volumes are published with the third edition (June 2005) of the ECC

- the complete Engineering and Construction Contract (ECC),
- the flow charts,
- these guidance notes, and
- six merged versions of the ECC, one for each main Option.

The complete ECC

This volume contains all the clauses and schedules comprising the ECC, including

- core clauses – common to all contracts,
- clauses for each of the main Options A to F – one of which must be chosen for a particular contract,
- clauses for the two alternative dispute resolution, Options W1 and W2, one of which must be chosen,
- clauses for each of the secondary Options X1 to X7, X12 to X18, and X20 – each available, if required, for a particular contract,
- Schedule of Cost Components, applicable to main Options C, D and E,
- Shorter Schedule of Cost Components, applicable to main Options A to E, and
- Contract Data formats parts one and two.

Flow charts

The flow charts show the procedural logic on which the ECC is based. They are available for reference in conjunction with these guidance notes.

Merged versions

Each merged version includes the clauses for the relevant main Option located in their appropriate places among the core clauses. Thus, the conditions for each main Option can be read together. The main Option clauses are in bold print for easy identification.

The merged versions also include

- the dispute resolution Option clauses
- those secondary Option clauses which can be used with each main option,
- the Contract Data, adapted for each main Option,
- either both Schedules of Cost Components (for Options C, D and E) or only the Shorter Schedule of Cost Components (for Options A and B) or neither (for Option F).

Clause numbering

The ECC is arranged in nine sections

1 General
2 The *Contractor*'s main responsibilities
3 Time
4 Testing and Defects
5 Payment
6 Compensation events
7 Title
8 Risks and insurance
9 Termination

The first digit of a clause number, whether for a core clause or a main Option clause, is the number of the section to which the clause belongs. A clause may be subdivided, for example Clause 16 includes four separate parts, numbered 16.1 to 16.4. Reference in these guidance notes to Clause 16 is a reference to all the parts of the clause; reference to Clause 16.2 is to that part only.

Where a clause is used in more than one main Option, the same number is used. The number of a clause, whether core or optional, is unique to the text of the paragraph.

The two alternative dispute resolution Option clauses are numbered W1 and W2.

The secondary Option clauses are numbered separately. The prefix 'X' is used for secondary Options that can be used in any country. For secondary Options that are specific to the country in which the works are carried out or the country of the *law of the contract*, the prefix 'Y' is used followed by a further prefix to denote the country; for example Y(UK) denotes a secondary Option that is applicable to, at least parts of, the United Kingdom. Any additional secondary clauses that are required for a specific project should be numbered with the prefix 'Z'.

The tables in Appendix 1 of these guidance notes illustrate the integration of the main Option clauses and paragraphs within the core clauses and list the dispute resolution clauses and the secondary Option clauses.

Project organisation

The project organisation assumed in the ECC involves the participants shown in Figure 1.

The ECC is used for the contract between the *Employer* and the *Contractor*. The *Contractor* may use the ECS, ECSS or PSC for his subcontracts. The PSC may be used for the *Employer*'s contracts with the *Project Manager*, the designers and the *Supervisor*. The NEC Adjudicator's Contract is used for the contract between the *Employer* and *Contractor* (jointly) and the *Adjudicator*. It may also be used in subcontracts using any NEC form of contract.

The roles of the *Project Manager*, *Employer*'s designers and *Supervisor* may be combined where the objectives of the *Employer* are served by so doing. Similarly, any or all of these three roles may be taken by employees of the *Employer*. The role of the *Adjudicator* should neither be combined with another role nor taken by an employee of the *Employer*.

The obligation of the *Project Manager* to make rapid decisions means that the *Employer* must give him considerable authority. An understanding of the *Employer*'s internal procedures is also an advantage. For some employers this will mean that the *Project Manager* will come from the *Employer*'s organisation, although staff from a consultant can be considered. A solution adopted by many employers is to appoint one of their staff as the *Project Manager*, supported by a consultant's staff to whom the *Project Manager* delegates some of his actions.

The *Supervisor*'s role is more directly technical, and a consultant's staff are frequently appointed as *Supervisor*.

Roles and duties

The ECC sets out the responsibilities and roles of the following parties

- the *Employer*,
- the *Project Manager*,
- the *Supervisor*,
- the *Contractor*,
- Subcontractors, and
- the *Adjudicator*.

Separate functions of *Employer*'s designer and *Contractor*'s designer are assumed but not mentioned in the contract.

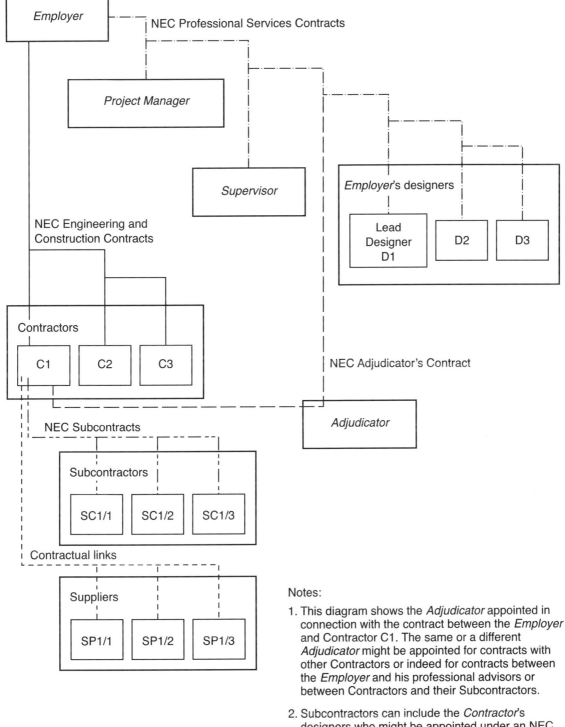

Notes:

1. This diagram shows the *Adjudicator* appointed in connection with the contract between the *Employer* and Contractor C1. The same or a different *Adjudicator* might be appointed for contracts with other Contractors or indeed for contracts between the *Employer* and his professional advisors or between Contractors and their Subcontractors.

2. Subcontractors can include the *Contractor*'s designers who might be appointed under an NEC Professional Services Contract between the *Contractor* and the designer rather than the ECC Subcontract shown in this diagram.

Figure 1. The NEC System – key players and contractual links.

The role played by the Engineer, Architect, Contract Administrator or Supervising Officer in other standard forms is divided between the *Project Manager*, the *Supervisor*, the *Employer*'s designer and the *Adjudicator*.

The *Project Manager*

The *Project Manager* is appointed by the *Employer*, either from his own staff or from outside. His role within the ECC is to manage the contract for the *Employer* with the intention of achieving the *Employer*'s objectives for the completed project

The *Employer* will normally appoint a project manager in the feasibility study stages of a project. His duties may then also include acting on behalf of the *Employer* and advising him on the procurement of design, on estimates of costs and time, on the merits of alternative schemes and on choosing the most appropriate contract strategy.

As contracts are placed for construction work, it is preferable to appoint the person or organisation already appointed for the whole project to act as the *Project Manager* on a particular contract. However, it is essential that the *Project Manager* for a particular contract is sufficiently close to the work and has the time and authority to carry out his duties effectively. On very large projects, especially those including several contracts, it may be necessary to appoint a different *Project Manager* for each contract or for the *Project Manager* to delegate his responsibilities for some of the contracts.

The ECC places considerable authority in the hands of the *Project Manager*. It assumes that he has the *Employer*'s authority to carry out the actions and make the decisions required of him. If his contract with the *Employer* constrains him in any way, as for example in the case of a limit on the amount which the *Project Manager* may authorise as a compensation event assessment, it is the responsibility of the *Project Manager* to ensure that all the approvals are given in time to enable him to comply with the time periods set out in the ECC. If such approvals by the *Employer* are not given, the *Contractor* has the right to raise the matter with the *Adjudicator*. It is not advisable to state limits on the *Project Manager*'s authority in the additional conditions of contract as this will make settlement of disputes difficult.

The *Project Manager* is free to seek the *Employer*'s views as much or as little as his relationship and contract with the *Employer* requires. He will normally maintain close contact with the *Employer* so that his decisions reflect the *Employer*'s business objectives. He has authority to change the work, to instruct the *Contractor* and generally to apply his managerial and engineering judgement. Positive management from both sides is encouraged.

In the special case of turnkey contracts, for which Option A is the only realistic main Option, the *Project Manager* will be expected to take a less active role. He should certainly avoid issuing instructions unless absolutely essential, as to do so is against the turnkey concept. No change is necessary to the wording of the conditions of contract but the *Employer* should be careful in describing the limits of what he expects the *Project Manager* to do in his contract with the *Project Manager*.

The contractual role of the *Project Manager* is defined in terms of the actions and decisions he is to take. He is constrained from acting unreasonably in this role by statements of the basis on which he is to make each type of decision but not what decisions he is to make. If the *Contractor* believes that any of the *Project Manager*'s actions or decisions is not in accordance with the contract, he may refer it to the *Adjudicator* (Option W1 or W2).

Perhaps the strongest feature of the ECC which stimulates co-operation rather than adversarial activity is the fact that the *Contractor* is little concerned financially with the way the *Project Manager* decides to deal with problems which are the *Employer*'s responsibility. If the *Contractor*'s eventual payment is largely secure, he is not encouraged to make the worst of any problems which arise, either as regards their effect upon cost or upon the timing of the work. This feature is strengthened by the flexibility available to the *Employer* and the *Project Manager* in their pre-contract choice of main Option for a particular contract ranging from price commitment to cost reimbursable. The ECC permits this choice of contract strategy without the need to resort to different standard forms.

Designers

Designers for the *Employer*'s design are appointed by the *Employer*. If several designers are appointed, possibly covering different disciplines, good practice requires that a lead designer be appointed.

If the design of the *works* depends on a process technology, for which the *Employer* has a licence, he will need to provide appropriate access to it as part of his contract with his designer or the *Contractor* (and also for management purposes in the *Project Manager*'s contract).

The *Employer*'s designer's role is to develop the design to meet the *Employer*'s objectives to the point where tenders for construction are to be invited. If a 'design and construct' contract is envisaged, the *Employer*'s designer's role is restricted largely to providing a performance specification together with standards for design and materials which he may wish to specify for inclusion in the Works Information.

Under the ECC, the *Employer*'s designer is not referred to in the contract between the *Employer* and the *Contractor*. However, the *Employer* should ensure that the *Project Manager*'s brief includes management of the designer's activities. The *Project Manager* should have ready access to the designer for advice.

On many civil engineering projects, particularly those involving work at or below ground level, it is important that the assumptions made by the designer are reviewed against the conditions actually encountered during construction. This is essential in high-risk operations such as tunnelling contracts. On such projects the role of the designer should not end when the Works Information is complete but should continue during construction in some capacity. This principle applies whether the design has been prepared for the *Employer* or for the *Contractor*.

In priced contracts (Options A and B), changes of the *Employer*'s design are dealt with as compensation events. In target contracts (Options C and D) they are also dealt with as compensation events, but their assessment only affects the Prices (the target) and hence the *Contractor*'s share, rather than the Price for Work Done to Date. (See explanatory notes on Clause 53 for Options C and D).

The *Supervisor*

The *Supervisor* is appointed by the *Employer* for a particular contract. He can be an in-house person or someone from outside. His role is defined in the ECC in terms of the actions and decisions he is to take. Essentially, his role is to check that the *works* are constructed in accordance with the contract. It is similar to that of a resident engineer or architect who may be assisted by an inspector of clerk of works. In some circumstances it would be appropriate for the clerk of works to carry out the role of *Supervisor*.

The *Supervisor* does have one significant contractual responsibility. It is his responsibility to issue the Defects Certificate, which signifies the end of most of the obligations of the Parties.

A disputed action by the *Supervisor,* like that of the *Project Manager*, can be referred by the *Contractor* to the *Adjudicator*.

The *Adjudicator*

The *Adjudicator*'s role, under either dispute resolution Option, is to settle any disputes that arise between the Parties quickly and efficiently. The intention is that disputes are dealt with quickly and not left to cause ill will amongst the Parties.

The Parties should therefore not look upon adjudication under the ECC as just another form of litigation but rather as an efficient method for referring honestly held differences, between parties working together in a spirit of mutual trust and co-operation, to an independent third party to decide. The *Adjudicator*'s decision is binding upon the Parties. If either Party does not accept that decision they have only a limited period to notify the other Party of their intention to refer the matter to the *tribunal*, after which it becomes final as well as binding.

It should also be noted that all disputes have first to be referred to the *Adjudicator* for his decision before they are referred to the *tribunal*.

The *Adjudicator* is appointed jointly by the *Employer* and the *Contractor*, preferably before work commences, using the NEC Adjudicator's Contract. The *Employer* should insert his choice of *Adjudicator* in part one of the Contract Data. If the *Contractor* does not agree with the choice, a suitable person will be the subject of discussion and agreement before the Contract Date. Alternatively, the *Employer* may propose a list of acceptable names, and the successful tenderer may be asked to select one of them to be *Adjudicator*. Some employers may prefer the tenderers to propose suitable names.

The *Adjudicator* becomes involved only when a dispute is referred to him. As a person independent of both *Employer* and *Contractor*, he is required by the contract he has with the Parties to give a decision on the dispute within stated time limits. Under the NEC Adjudicator's Contract, payment of the *Adjudicator*'s fee is shared equally by the Parties, unless otherwise agreed by the Parties.

CONTRACT STRATEGY

Choosing the strategy

The *Employer* (usually advised by the *Project Manager*) chooses the contract strategy for the project. He should review his choice later, when he starts preparing the tender documents for each contract. Factors taken into account in deciding what type of contract to use from within the NEC family include the following.

- Who has the necessary design expertise?
- Is there particular pressure to complete quickly?
- How important is performance of the completed *works*?
- Is certainty of final cost more important than lowest final cost?
- Where can a risk be best managed?
- What total risk is tolerable for contractors?
- How important is cross-contract co-ordination to achievement of project objectives?
- Does the *Employer* have good reasons for himself selecting specialist contractors or suppliers for parts of the work?

The result of these considerations should be a statement of the chosen contract strategy comprising the following

- a schedule of the parts of the project which will be let as separate contracts,
- for each contract – a statement of the stages of work which it will include covering management, design, manufacture, erection, construction, installation, testing and commissioning as appropriate, and
- a statement of the NEC contract which will be used for each contract, and, where relevant, which main Option will be used.

The ECC has six main Options, based on different mechanisms for payment to the *Contractor* and offering different basic allocations of risk between the *Employer* and the *Contractor*.

All the main Options can be used with the boundary between design by the *Employer* and design by the *Contractor* set to suit the chosen strategy. If the Works Information set down by the *Employer* is only a performance specification, most of the design will be done by the *Contractor* (effectively a 'design and construct' contract). If the Works Information includes detailed drawings and specifications, little design remains for the *Contractor* to complete.

An advantage of using the ECC is that, whatever variations in strategy are adopted, most of the procedures, based upon the core clauses of the ECC, will be common to all contracts.

The main Options

There are six types of payment mechanism available in the main Options:

Option A Priced contract with activity schedule
Option B Priced contract with bill of quantities
Option C Target contract with activity schedule
Option D Target contract with bill of quantities
Option E Cost reimbursable contract
Option F Management contract.

Each Option uses different arrangements for payment to the *Contractor* as each Option allocates risk differently between the *Employer* and the *Contractor*.

The extreme cases of risk allocation are the priced Options A and B on the one hand and the cost reimbursable Option E on the other hand. In the priced Options, the *Contractor* is paid at tendered prices (and rates with Option B) for the work he has done. He carries all risks other than the *Employer*'s risks stated in the contract and the financial and time effects of compensation events. In a cost reimbursable contract, the *Contractor* is paid the Defined Cost, as defined in the chosen main Option. The target Options C and D permit the cost risk to be shared between the *Employer* and the *Contractor*. The management Option F is essentially cost reimbursable but risk allocation can be varied by choosing appropriate main Options in the subcontracts.

The priced and target Options offer a choice between two types of pricing document, namely an *activity schedule* and a *bill of quantities*.

This range of choice covers most arrangements used in engineering and building construction. Construction management, in which the *Contractor* provides management services to the *Employer* but has no responsibility for construction work, is also provided for. In this case, the *Employer* appoints a construction management contractor as *Project Manager*. He then advises the *Employer* on placing trade or construction contracts using one of the main Options for each contract.

For a particular contract, one main Option is chosen. The optional clauses are combined with the core clauses to provide a complete contract. The core clauses cannot be used on their own. They are clauses which are common to the types of contract covered by the main Options.

The following are brief summaries of the main characteristics and uses of each main Option. Further notes on the preparation of the various documents are given under 'Tender documents'. Further explanation is given in the explanatory notes for Sections 5 and 6.

Option A: Priced contract with activity schedule

An *activity schedule* is a list of activities prepared by the *Contractor* which he expects to carry out in Providing the Works. When it has been priced by the *Contractor*, the lump sum for each activity is the Price to be paid by the *Employer* for that activity. The total of these Prices is the *Contractor*'s price for providing the whole of the *works*, including for all matters which are at the *Contractor*'s risk. Option A provides for stage payments (see notes under 'Tender documents').

Option B: Priced contract with bill of quantities

A *bill of quantities* comprises a list of work items and quantities. It is prepared by or for the *Employer*. Standard methods of measurement are published which state the items to be included and how the quantities are to be measured and calculated.

Tenderers price the items, taking account of the information in the tender documents and including for all matters which are at the *Contractor*'s risk. The *Employer* pays for work done on the basis of actual measurement of those items with quantities.

Options C and D: Target contracts (with activity schedule or bill of quantities)

Target contracts are sometimes used where the extent of work to be done is not fully defined or where anticipated risks are greater. The financial risk is shared between the *Employer* and the *Contractor* in the following way:

- The *Contractor* tenders a target price in the form of the Prices using either the *activity schedule* or a *bill of quantities*. The target price includes the *Contractor*'s estimate of Defined Cost plus other costs, overheads and profit to be covered by his Fee.
- The *Contractor* tenders his Fee in terms of fee percentages to be applied to Defined Cost.

- During the course of the contract, the *Contractor* is paid Defined Cost plus the Fee. This is defined as the Price for Work Done to Date (PWDD) (see explanatory notes on Section 5).

The Prices are adjusted for the effects of compensation events, and for inflation if Option X1 is used; for Option D the Prices are also adjusted as the work completed by the *Contractor* is measured.

At the end of the contract, the *Contractor* is paid (or pays) his share of the difference between the final total of the Prices and the final PWDD according to a formula stated in the Contract Data. If the final PWDD is greater than the final total of the Prices, the *Contractor* pays his share of the difference. The *Contractor*'s share is paid provisionally at Completion and is corrected in the final account.

(See explanatory notes on Clause 53.)

Option E: Cost reimbursable contract

A cost reimbursable contract should be used when the definition of the work to be done is inadequate even as a basis for a target price and yet an early start to construction is required. In such circumstances, the *Contractor* cannot be expected to take cost risks other than those which entail control of his employees and other resources. He carries minimum risk and is paid Defined Cost plus his tendered Fee, subject only to a small number of constraints designed to motivate efficient working.

Option F: Management contract

The conditions of contract applied to management contracts are still evolving. In practice there are several different approaches used in relation to, for example, scope of services, time of appointment and methods of fee payment. The terms under which subcontractors are employed are also changing. The ECC management contract is based on the following framework.

The *Contractor*'s responsibilities for construction work are the same as those of a *Contractor* working under one of the other Options. However, he does only the limited amount of construction work himself as stated in the Contract Data. The *Project Manager* has no authority to instruct the *Contractor* to carry out further construction work beyond that stated in the Contract Data. Any increase in the extent of the construction work to be carried out by the *Contractor* must be the subject of negotiation between the *Employer* and the *Contractor*.

The *Contractor*'s services apply mainly to the construction phase, although he would usually be appointed before construction starts. If substantial pre-construction services are required and the *Employer* wishes to have the option to change the Management Contractor before construction starts, a separate contract should be awarded for such pre-construction services, using the NEC Professional Services Contract.

All subcontracts are direct contracts with the *Contractor*, who acts as a Management Contractor. If the *Employer* wishes to be a party to the construction subcontracts, a management contract is not appropriate. He should instead appoint a construction manager as the *Project Manager* and use the ECC with appropriate main Options for the contracts with package contractors.

The *Contractor* tenders his Fee and his estimated total of the Prices of the subcontracts. The subcontract prices are paid to the *Contractor* as part of Defined Cost. The *Contractor* is responsible for supplying management services, including the management of design if required. If the *Contractor* wishes to be responsible for doing work other than management he must state the extent of that work in the Contract Data (see notes on Clause 20.2).

The *Contractor*'s Fee will increase if Subcontractors' prices (part of Defined Cost to the *Contractor*) increase due to compensation events. However, he will not receive separate payment for his work in dealing with compensation events and he will not receive any additional Fee for work on compensation events which does not lead to an increase in Subcontractors' prices.

The dispute resolution Options

There are two Options for dispute resolution. Option W2 is to be used for UK contracts to which the provisions of the Housing Grants, Construction and Regeneration Act 1996 apply. Option W1 is to be used in all other cases.

The secondary Options

After deciding the main Option, the user may choose any of the secondary Options that are available for the chosen main Option. It is not necessary to use any of them. The chosen secondary Options, together with the chosen main Option, must be identified in the first statement of part one of the Contract Data. The secondary Options are

Option X1	Price adjustment for inflation (used only with Options A, B, C and D)
Option X2	Changes in the law
Option X3	Multiple currencies (used only with Options A and B)
Option X4	Parent company guarantee
Option X5	Sectional Completion
Option X6	Bonus for early Completion
Option X7	Delay damages
Option X12	Partnering
Option X13	Performance bond
Option X14	Advanced payment to the *Contractor*
Option X15	Limitation of the *Contractor*'s liability for his design to reasonable skill and care
Option X16	Retention (not used with Option F)
Option X17	Low performance damages
Option X18	Limitation of liability
Option X20	Key Performance Indicators (not used with Option X12)
Option Y(UK)2	The Housing Grants, Construction and Regeneration Act 1996
Option Y(UK)3	The Contract (Rights of Third Parties) Act 1999
Option Z	*Additional conditions of contract.*

Choice of Options

The sequence of decisions to be taken in choosing the main and secondary Options for a particular contract are illustrated in Figure 2.

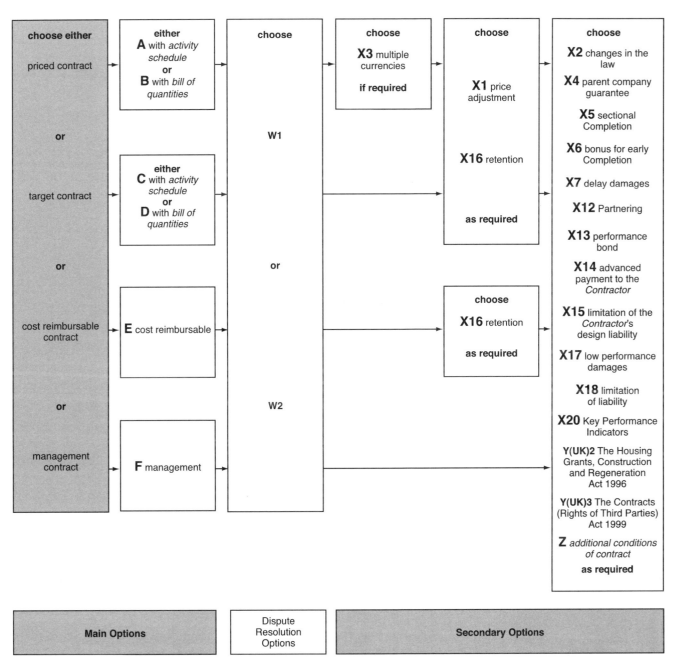

Figure 2. Options using the NEC Engineering and Construction Contract.

TENDER DOCUMENTS

Preparing the tender documents

Deciding the contracts

Having decided the contract strategy, the *Employer* is able to decide which contracts he requires to carry out the project, what types of contract to use (choosing from the main Options A to F in each case), how they relate to each other in time and physically and what secondary Options he will use for each contract.

The tender documents

It is not necessary to issue the ECC printed documents to tenderers as they are incorporated by reference in the Contract Data. The documents to be issued with invitations to tender include the following.

- Instructions to tenderers (including any instructions for preparing the *activity schedule* under Options A and C).
- A form of tender.
- Contract Data part one.
- Contract Data part two (pro-forma for completion by tenderers).
- *Bill of quantities* (Options B and D).
- Works Information.
- Site Information.
- A pre-tender health and safety plan is normally required for UK contracts.

Form of tender

No standard form of tender has been included in the ECC as many *Employers* have standard forms containing their own requirements. A suggested form is included in Appendix 2.

Contract Data

In the clauses of the ECC, the term Contract Data refers to the data which exist at the Contract Date. These are not necessarily those originally issued by the *Employer* (part one) or returned as part of the successful tenderer's offer (part two); they are sometimes changed during negotiations between the *Employer* and the potential *Contractor*. The Contract Data define the details of the agreement which is the contract. The conditions of contract make provision for certain changes, such as replacement of key people, change of Completion Date or Key Date and replacement of the *Adjudicator*.

The purpose of the Contract Data is to provide data as required by the *conditions of contract* specific to a particular contract. The terms in italics in the *conditions of contract* must be identified in the Contract Data in accordance with Clause 11.1. The Contract Data is a key document in any contract using the ECC.

The format for both parts one and two of the Contract Data for a particular contract enquiry should be assembled by the *Employer* using the formats and wording for each statement as set out in the ECC, with spaces adjusted appropriately. As well as the statements to be given in all contracts, the selected optional statements should be included (preferably within the statements for the relevant Section of the ECC) but omitting the explanatory sentences printed in bold type and commencing 'If', which are only for the guidance of users. Data for the Shorter Schedule of Cost Components is required for all Options except Option F; data for the Schedule of Cost Components is only required for Options C, D and E.

In order to avoid lengthy entries for certain statements, it may be convenient to list them in a separate document which is clearly referenced in the Contract Data. For example, a schedule of drawings could be referred to in the Contract Data rather than reproduced it in full.

Part one

This is completed by the *Employer* for each contract. Worked examples are given in Appendix 5.

The opening statement in '1 General' identifies the clauses in the conditions of contract for a particular contract.

Part two

This part contains a list of data to be supplied by tenderers as part of their offer. Certain information is to be given in all contracts.

Optional statements follow, from which the *Employer* will have selected those he requires. For instance, the statement regarding the *completion date* should be included only if the *Employer* has not fixed the *completion date* in the Contract Data part one and wishes tenderers to submit their proposals.

The tendered total of the Prices must be entered where Option A, B, C or D is used. This will be transferred from the grand total of the *activity schedule* or *bill of quantities* as the case may be. In assessing tenders, it is most important that the total entered in the Contract Data is checked against the total of the *activity schedule* or *bill of quantities*.

The data for the Schedule of Cost Components comprise information to be tendered relating to calculation of Defined Cost. This is required to assess compensation events and to calculate payments due to the *Contractor* in Options C, D and E. The cost component data for use with the Shorter Schedule of Cost Components, which are also part of a *Contractor*'s tender, can only be used for assessing compensation events.

The information submitted by tenderers in part two of the Contract Data is used in assessing tenders. (For *works* which fall within European Community legislation, the publication of award criteria is a requirement of the procurement directive, and award criteria are normally explained in the instructions to tenderers.)

Activity schedule
General use with Options A
and C

This document is prepared and priced by tenderers. Its use varies between Options A and C. It is not part of the Works Information and must not be used to describe the *works*.

The prices entered by the tenderers for each activity are lump sums, not unit rates as in a *bill of quantities*. The tenderer decides how to break up his work into activities, enters them on the schedule and prices each one. If the *Employer* wants to specify particular activities which the *Contractor* is to identify in the *activity schedule* he may do so, stating his requirements in the instructions to tenderers.

For the purpose of comparing tenders it can be useful to define principal activities (for example individual structures or specific lengths of new road) and invite tenderers to subdivide each into activities of their own choosing.

Tenderers should be reminded that not all activities in an activity schedule will be direct construction activities; there may be design activities, administrative activities, testing, etc.

Use of Options A and C of the ECC does not require a bill of quantities to be issued to tenderers or to be used subsequently. Consequently, tenderers have to calculate quantities from the Works Information where they need to know a quantity in order to estimate the cost of the work. For many contracts (including process plant, building construction, etc.) this is a significant task.

In order to reduce the cost and time involved during the tender preparation period, *Employers* may wish to calculate quantities before inviting tenders and then issue a copy of the quantities list to all tenderers. When this is done, it must be made clear that the tenderer will have used the quantities and relied upon them entirely at his own risk of their inaccuracy or incompleteness. No amendment to the contract or addition to the contract is necessary to achieve this as the contract is clear that the *Contractor*'s obligation is to carry out the work described in the Works Information. There is no mechanism for this obligation to be qualified or modified by the issue of quantities to tenderers.

Some *Employers* issue quantities and instruct tenderers to base their *activity schedules* on these quantities. Once the successful tenderer has been identified, the parties together agree any changes to those quantities which may be necessary, and any changes to the prices for the relevant activities which may follow. This has the advantage of letting tenderers concentrate on pricing the work and not worrying about possible errors in quantities. Once the contract has been formed change in quantities is one of the *Contractor*'s risks, as normal.

Option A Instructions to tenderers

The following or similar text should be included in instructions to tenderers for Option A enquiries.

Activity schedule

Tenderers are to submit an *activity schedule* with their tenders. This will be a document headed '*activity schedule*' and will comprise a list of activities with an amount entered against each activity. This amount is the sum due to the *Contractor* on completion of each activity unless it is included in a group. If groups of activities are required to be identified on the schedule, payment for each group becomes due when all the activities in that group are completed.

Activity descriptions must be clear and complete so that the work included in each can be identified and the completion of each activity easily recognised.

Note also the requirement of Clause 31.4 of the conditions of contract about the relationship between the *activity schedule* and the programme.

The following activities must be included in the schedule but may be subdivided:

[List of particular activities to be identified.]

The following groups of activities must be identified in the schedule.

[List of groups of activities to be identified.]

Use with Option C

With Option C there is little point in requiring groups of activities to be identified because the *activity schedule* in Option C is not used directly for payment purposes. It is used to adjust the Prices when compensation events occur and subsequently for calculating the *Contractor*'s share after Completion (see Clause 53).

Bill of quantities
General use with Options B and D

The *method of measurement*, on which the *bill of quantities* is based, is identified in part one of the Contract Data. This should also include identification of any amendments or additions to the standard *method of measurement*.

The *bill of quantities* is to be priced and extended by tenderers, to produce the tendered total of the Prices.

There is no general provision for payment for Equipment or Plant and Materials within the Working Areas before they are incorporated into the *works*, i.e. equivalent to 'materials on site'. The *Contractor* may wish to receive earlier payment to improve his cash flow. The required effect can be obtained under Option B by inserting appropriate items in the method related charges where the *method of measurement* allows or, alternatively, making allowance in the rates of the *bill of quantities* for the financing of the Equipment or Plant and Materials until they are incorporated in the *works*. The special circumstances under which payment might be made for Equipment or Plant and Materials which are outside the Working Areas are covered in Section 7.

It is important that the *bill of quantities* should be prepared to suit the position at which the boundary between the *Employer*'s and the *Contractor*'s design is set for each contract. All the standard methods of measurement which are available assume that the *Employer* is responsible for most of the design. The rules for itemisation and description of the work are set accordingly.

Consequently, when using ECC with the *Contractor* carrying out more design, the existing methods of measurement must be amended or a special method of measurement substituted. In extreme cases, such as when the *Contractor* is carrying out most of the design, a *bill of quantities* is not appropriate and an *activity schedule* (i.e. Option A or Option C) should be used.

For example, standard methods of measurement usually require separate items to be given for concrete, reinforcement and formwork in reinforced concrete, with quantities for each. When the *Contractor* is to design the reinforced concrete, it is impossible for the *Employer* to calculate the quantities before he is appointed. It is also contractually inappropriate as the *Contractor* takes the risk of quantity variation for items which he has designed. The principle which must be followed is that the items in the *bill of quantities* must not describe the work using any assumptions about what the *Contractor* may choose to provide or about the quantities of work which he will choose to provide.

Tender document in cost reimbursable contracts General use with Options E and F

If the *Contractor* for a cost reimbursable contract is selected by competitive tendering, the basis on which tenders are selected should be clearly stated in the invitation to tender. Award criteria will include the level of the *fee percentages* tendered and the various percentages tendered as cost component data. For this purpose, provisional estimates of Defined Cost should be included in a tender document together with provisional amounts to which the various tendered percentages in the cost component data are applied. This will provide a notional tender price on which tenders can be assessed.

Works Information

The documents containing the Works Information provided by the *Employer* are identified in part one of the Contract Data. Any Works Information for the *Contractor*'s design submitted by tenderers with their tenders is to be identified in part two of the Contract Data.

Most of this information will be given in a specification and on drawings in the traditional manner. Where information is provided by non-documentary means such as models, they should be identified and their availability and location stated.

The Works Information in part one of the Contract Data should include the following items. The related contract clause numbers are given in brackets.

Description of *works*

- A general description of the *works*, including general arrangement and location drawings.

- Working/production and other detailed drawings, specification, models and other means used to describe the parts of the *works* designed by the Employer.
- A statement of any constraints on how the *Contractor* Provides the Works, e.g. restrictions on access, sequences of construction.

Plant and Materials	<ul><li>Materials and workmanship specifications.</li><li>Requirements for delivery and storage before the incorporation of Plant and Materials in the *works*, provision of spares and the specification of the vendor data required. This can conveniently be included in the specification.</li></ul>
Health and safety [27.4]	Any particular health and safety requirements, such as the safety regulations for the factory within which the Site is located. Any health and safety plan for the project, as may be required by statute, should also be included.
Contractor's design [21.1]	A statement of those parts of the *works* which the *Contractor* is to design. The form of this statement will depend on the extent of the *Contractor's* design responsibility. For contracts with little *Contractor's* design, a list of what is left to be designed by the *Contractor* should be provided. For more comprehensive design and construct contracts, a list of what has been designed by the *Employer* should be given, with the *Contractor* being made responsible for designing the remainder.
[21.2]	A design brief or performance specification for those parts of the *works* to be designed by the *Contractor*, including <ul><li>size or space limitations,</li><li>design standards and codes of practice,</li><li>materials and workmanship specifications, including references to relevant standards,</li><li>loading and capacity requirements, and</li><li>operational performance requirements and design life.</li></ul>
[21.2]	Procedures which the *Contractor* is to follow in carrying out his design. Particulars of the design which are to be submitted to the *Project Manager*, including requirements for certification and/or checking.
[22.1]	The purposes for which the *Employer* may require to use and copy the *Contractor's* design.
Completion [11.2(2)]	The work required to be done by the Completion Date for the whole of the *works* and, if Option X5 is used, for each of the *sections*. Alternatively, this could be in the form of a list of work which can remain undone at the Completion Date.
Working with the *Employer* and Others [25.1]	Details of Others who will be occupying the Working Areas during the contract period indicating which parts they will occupy and for what periods.
[25.2]	The services and other things which the *Employer* and the *Contractor* are to provide to each other and to Others while the *Contractor* has access to and use of the Site.
Subcontracting [26]	<ul><li>Lists of acceptable subcontractors for particular tasks.</li><li>Statement of any work which should not be subcontracted.</li><li>Statement of any work which is required to be subcontracted.</li></ul>
Programme [31.2]	Any information which the *Contractor* is required to include in the programme in addition to that already stated in Clause 31.2.

On multi-contract projects, it will probably be necessary for the *Contractor* to provide boundary data, foundation design data, 'hook-up' data and similar information relating to his design for the use of the *Employer* and other contractors. The times when this information is to be submitted should be stated in accordance with the overall programme for the project. Alternatively this can be achieved by the use of the Key Dates.

Tests	[40.1]	Descriptions of the tests to be carried out by the *Contractor*, the *Supervisor* and Others, including those which must be done before Completion.
	[40.2]	Details of materials, facilities and samples to be provided by the *Contractor* and by the *Employer* for tests.
	[41.1]	Details of Plant and Materials which are to be inspected or tested before delivery to the Working Areas, including details of the inspection or test.
	[41.1]	Definition of tests of Equipment, Plant and Materials outside the Working Areas which have to be passed before marking by the *Supervisor*.
	[71.1]	Details of the preparation of Equipment, Plant and Materials for marking by the *Supervisor*.
Title	[73.2]	Statement of any materials from excavation and demolition to which the *Contractor* will have title.
Damage to highways, etc.		Note that no equivalent to Clause 30 of the ICE Conditions of Contract is included as this is a special case of third party damage which is covered in Section 8.

If Option C, D, E or F is used

Acceptance or procurement procedures	[11.2(25) or (26)]	Any acceptance or procurement procedures to be followed by the *Contractor*.
Accounts and records	[52.2]	Details of records to be kept by the *Contractor* other than those already stated in Clause 52.2.

If Option X4 is used

Parent company guarantee	[X4.1]	The form of the guarantee.

If Option X13 is used

Performance bond	[X13.1]	The form of the performance bond.

If Option X14 is used

Advanced payment bond	[X14.2]	The form of the advanced payment bond (if required).

If Option X17 is used

Performance test	[X17.1]	Details of any test to be used to measure the performance of the *works* or an item of Plant for which low performance damages are specified.
Site Information		The documents in which the Site Information is contained are identified in part one of the Contract Data. Site Information may include the following.

- Subsoil investigation borehole records and test results.
- Reports obtained by the Employer concerning the physical conditions within the Site or its surroundings. This may include mapping, hydrographic data and hydrological information.

- References to publicly available information about the Site and its surroundings, such as published papers and interpretations of the Geological Survey. The purpose of listing these references is to help a tenderer to prepare his tender, to decide his method of working and programme and prepare any designs for which he would be responsible. Normally only factual information about physical conditions on the Site and its surroundings is included in the Site Information. Interpretation is a matter for the *Contractor*. However, some *Employers* may wish to include interpretative information, such as inferred geological sections.
- Information about plant and services below the surface of the Site.
- Information about piped and other services.
- Information about buildings, structures, plant (including machinery) adjacent to and on the Site.

Some documents may contain both Works Information and Site Information. For example, a drawing may show a foundation and related borehole information. Such a document should be identified in the Contract Data both as a document containing Works Information and as a document containing Site Information.

Because of the definition of Works Information and Site Information, it should not be necessary to detail which parts of such a document fall into each category.

Inviting and preparing tenders

Instructions to tenderers

When it is intended that the *Contractor* will carry out design work, the *Employer* may wish tendering contractors to submit information about their proposed design with their tenders. It is then included in part two of the Contract Data. If they do, the instructions to tenderers must include particulars of the information required. It is not essential to ask for any such information as the provisions of the ECC are designed so that the contract obligations and procedures are unaffected by the amount of pre-tender design carried out by tenderers, but it is important that enough information is provided to allow the *Employer* to verify that a tenderer's design appears to be sound. In any event, no more pre-tender design than is regarded by the *Employer* as essential should be asked for because, for all but one of the tenderers, the work will be abortive and an unrecovered cost. All tenderers will, of course, carry out such pre-tender design work as they decide is necessary to calculate their tendered prices.

The instructions to tenderers must also state which management functions are to be covered by the people who are to be identified in the Contract Data as key people.

The documents which tenderers will be required to submit will depend on which of the main Options A to F and of the secondary Options have been incorporated. In all cases, a complete form of tender will be required together with part two of the Contract Data. A suggested form of tender is included in Appendix 2.

Part two of the Contract Data

The statements to be given by the tenderer in all contracts are as follows.

- Name and address of the *Contractor*.

- The *fee percentages* (Clause 11.2(8)).
  These are tendered figures and will be taken into account in tender assessment (see later notes).

- Working Areas
  The tenderer is invited to specify areas other than the Site that he wishes to be included as *working areas*. However these *working areas* will not be considered to be Working Areas unless they comply with the definition in Clause 11.2(18).

- Key people
  A list of names, job descriptions, responsibilities, qualifications and experience of key people is required. The *Employer* should indicate in the instructions to tenderers for whom in the tenderer's organisation these details are required. The *Contractor* has no incentive to insert details of more than the minimum number of key people since each stated name and position constrains him. Sometimes these details are finalised during pre-contract negotiations between *Employer* and *Contractor*.

- The Works Information for the *Contractor*'s design.
  If the *Contractor* is not required to carry out any design or if the *Employer* does not wish the *Contractor* to submit any pre-tender design, there will be no entry under this heading. Where the *Contractor* is required to submit a large part of the design, the entry will comprise a list of drawings and specifications accompanying the tender.

  It is neither necessary nor desirable to require full working drawings in most cases, but the submission should be sufficient to enable the *Employer* to assess the design which each tenderer is offering.

Further statements will depend on which Options apply to the contract, and what information the *Employer* requires to be submitted with the tenders. These may include the following.

Programme

The programme reference number or title should be given and the programme submitted as a separate document. The main purpose of requiring submission of a programme with each tender is to inform the *Employer* of how the tenderer proposes to carry out the work and how it affects the *Employer*'s other contracts and activities.

Completion date

If a *completion date* is to be proposed by the tenderer this should be stated in the Contract Data part two, having been calculated from the *starting date* and taking account of the *access dates* stated by the *Employer* in the Contract Data part one.

Activity schedule (Options A and C)

A reference number or title should be given and the *activity schedule* submitted as a separate document. The *Employer* should state in the instructions to tenderers any activities or groups of activities he requires to be included.

Bill of quantities (Options B and D)

The *Contractor* enters a reference to the priced *bill of quantities* which is being included in his tender.

<table>
<tr><td>Tendered total of the Prices</td><td>For priced and target contracts (Options A, B, C and D), the tendered total should be entered. This will comprise the total of the bill of quantities or activity schedule as the case may be. The total of a bill of quantities will be subject to remeasurement and correction in accordance with the method of measurement.

The instructions to tenderers should include details of how the Employer will deal with any discrepancy between the total of the bill of quantities or the activity schedule and the total entered in the Contract Data, and how any arithmetical errors in tenders will be corrected.</td></tr>
<tr><td>Data for the Schedule of Cost Components</td><td>For main Options C, D and E, the details under this heading are entered by the tenderers. The percentages entered are not equivalent to the dayworks percentages in a conventional contract. (See explanatory notes on the Schedule of Cost Components).</td></tr>
<tr><td>Data for the Shorter Schedule of Cost Components</td><td>Details under this heading are entered by tenderers for all main Options except Option F.</td></tr>
<tr><td>Site investigations by tenderers</td><td>If the Contractor will be responsible for the design of the works, or a significant part of the works, tenderers may need or wish to carry out their own site investigation work. The Employer should consider how this can be done most efficiently and effectively.

In general terms, there are three possible different approaches.</td></tr>
</table>

1 Leave it to the tenderers, so that each carries out whatever investigations he thinks necessary. (Sometimes tenderers will combine in these circumstances to reduce their costs.)
2 At an early stage in the tender period, ask the tenderers to specify what site investigation work they require, and then arrange for a single site investigation to be carried out by or on behalf of the *Employer* to cover (within reason) the requirements of all the tenderers.
3 Leave any supplementary site investigation until after the contract has been formed.

Leaving the responsibility entirely with the tenderers is the easiest option from the *Employer*'s point of view. His role is then limited to arranging access to the site for the various site investigation contractors used by the tenderers. It may be a sensible option if widely differing design solutions are anticipated, but otherwise it is clearly inefficient and overall wastes money.

Organising an investigation by the *Employer* to satisfy the reasonable requirements of the tenderers is a more efficient option. The site investigation contractor can be appointed in advance, with only the details of the investigation to be confirmed, so there is no delay. (The basic outlines of the investigation can be reasonably estimated in advance, and this information is normally offered to the tenderers as a basis from which they will ask for additional work.)

Leaving detailed site investigation until the contract has been formed is a viable option in some circumstances. Where it would be difficult to carry out site investigation during the tender period, it may be the only choice. This might arise where for example there are difficulties in gaining access to the Site in advance of the contract, or where marine investigations cannot be carried out because of the time of year. Normally in these circumstances the *Employer* carries out some work and instructs tenderers to base their tenders on it. This can be done by the use of reference conditions – effectively stating boundary values for certain geotechnical parameters which the *Employer* 'guarantees'. The *Contractor* carries out site investigation work as part of the contract, and if these demonstrate that the conditions lie outside the reference condition boundaries the *Contractor* notifies a compensation event.

Incorporating the results of such site investigation works into the contract is discussed under the heading 'Creating the contract'; see below.

Employers and contractors are reminded that while it is generally possible to identify soil or rock parameters that influence or control design, it is more difficult to identify those that influence construction methods and cost. For example, rock strength may govern foundation design but does not necessarily indicate how difficult excavation will be.

Assessing tenders

Award criteria

To ensure equal treatment of all tenderers and to assist in their understanding of the *Employer*'s requirements, the criteria upon which tenders are to be assessed, and the weight given to the various tendered elements, should be clearly stated in the instructions to tenderers. These criteria can be in the form of a 'Tender Assessment Sheet'. An example of such a sheet suitable for use with Options A and B is given in Appendix 4.

Procurement law

If the contract is subject to procurement legislation, there may be a requirement to assess tenders on the basis of objective criteria made available to all tenderers. All relevant criteria should therefore be published, as it may infringe the law if other criteria, however commercially or technically desirable, are used to select the *Contractor*.

General law

In some jurisdictions, publication of assessment criteria may create an implied requirement that the published criteria must be followed by the *Employer*. Thus even if specific procurement legislation does not apply, all relevant factors should be stated, including those not readily quantifiable, such as aesthetic considerations.

Assessing target cost tenders

As with any tender assessment process, the aim is to identify the tenderer most likely to be able to assist the *Employer* to realise his aims for the project. These are usually completion of the work on time, within the budget, safely and to the quality required by the *Employer*. Target cost contracts pose particular problems to assessors in respect of final project cost.

Payments to the *Contractor* in Option C or Option D contracts are not based on tendered rates and prices for elements of work completed; they are based on the costs incurred by the *Contractor* in doing the work. The unit costs of the basic resources (people, Equipment, materials) will be very similar whichever tenderer becomes the *Contractor*. If they are building the *Employer*'s design, differences in the final cost of the project will depend on the efficiency with which the *Contractor* selects and uses the resources and his Fee. However, if the *Contractor* is also responsible for the design, there will be significant differences between the resources needed to implement the various design solutions offered.

It follows that in 'design and construct' contracts the tender assessment will focus primarily on the tenderers' designs, while in 'construct only' contracts the tenderers' method statements, Fee and other percentages quoted by tenderers will be the key elements to be compared. In both cases any qualifications made by tenderers must also be taken into account.

It is essential that the instructions to tenderers include requirements for tenderers to submit the information necessary for there to be a meaningful assessment and comparison of the tenders received. It may also be a requirement of applicable procurement rules that only criteria that are stated in the instructions to tenderers may be taken into account in the tender evaluation.

In requiring tenderers to submit information for tender evaluation purposes, it is important to retain a sense of scale and not to require extensive details of method statements, cost breakdowns etc. for comparatively small projects.

Assessing design and construct tenders

The key questions to be answered in the tender evaluation are as follows.

- Does the tenderer's design satisfy the requirements set out in the tender document?
- Can it be built in time and safely?
- Has the tenderer taken realistic account of the risks inherent in the project and developed robust solutions?
- Is the forecast cost (the tender total) a reasonable estimate?
- What is the likely cost of future maintenance?

It is important to give tenderers some criteria for the assessment of maintenance cost; it should really form part of the design requirements. It is important that the assessment made in the tender evaluation is, as far as possible, objective and numerical.

The tenderer whose aggregate construction cost + maintenance cost is lowest should be selected, provided the answers to the first four questions are positive.

It is not unusual for the answers to be 'yes – but'. The tender submissions may have design shortcomings or what appear to be unrealistically optimistic programmes. There is no hard and fast rule for dealing with such problems, but most approaches involve pricing what is necessary to make the tender compliant and using an adjusted tender price for tender comparison purposes. This is done by the tender evaluation team without involving tenderers, who would otherwise have a second opportunity to improve their submission.

Assessing construct only tenders

Tender evaluation will have two components – technical and commercial.

The technical assessment will attempt to verify that the tenderer's proposals are realistic and practical. In target cost tenders the commercial review will concentrate on the Fee and other percentages submitted by the different tenderers.

The Working Areas overheads percentage may vary widely between tenderers, one reason being the treatment of subcontractors. The percentage is applied to the cost of people. A tenderer having a high proportion of subcontracted work will have a low people cost, and a correspondingly high percentage figure for Working Areas overheads.

Qualified tenders

There is no difference between the treatment of tender qualifications in target cost contracts and their treatment in conventional contracts. Any qualifications, be they technical or commercial, are effectively uninvited tender offers. They are normally treated by assessing the cost of removing the qualifications to produce a fully compliant tender. The cost is added to the tendered price to produce a corrected price which is then used for tender comparison purposes.

Finalising the contract

Although design shortcomings and/or qualifications are costed and a revised tender price used in the evaluation, once a tenderer has been selected the contract must be finalised prior to award. This means that any design problems and qualifications have to be addressed.

One method of doing this is to treat each as an option; the tenderer has offered what he thinks the *Employer* might accept, but the *Employer* has an option to purchase what he actually requires by adding to the tendered price. Accepting all the options would mean that all the qualifications were removed. However, before finalising the contract it would be necessary to change the *Employer*'s Works Information to comply with the *Contractor*'s design since the *Employer*'s Works Information has priority over the *Contractor*'s Works Information.

If this approach is adopted, the selected tenderer must be invited to price the options which until now have only been costed by the tender evaluation team. No price higher than that used in arriving at the adjusted tender total should be accepted, because that would invalidate the basis of the selection of the tenderer.

Creating the contract

Frequently, negotiations with one or more tenderers are necessary to clarify intentions, to agree amendments, to eliminate qualifications which are not acceptable to the *Employer* and to discuss the *Contractor*'s design. It is important to minimise these negotiations since extended discussions can result in abuse of the tendering process. This can be achieved by careful preparation of tender documents and instructions to tenderers and by stating award criteria in objective terms.

The creation of a contract can be by means of acceptance of a tender or a revised tender or by means of acceptance by the *Contractor* of a counter-offer prepared by or on behalf of the *Employer*. A binding contract is thus created, although some *Employers* may require such acceptance being subject to a formal agreement. A suitable form of agreement is included in Appendix 3, but *Employers* often have their own standard forms. Essentially they record the agreement between the two Parties and identify the documents which make up the contract.

The Contract Data makes provision for the *Contractor*'s tender design to be incorporated into the contract as Works information (see Contact Data part two, first optional statement). There is no equivalent provision for any '*Contractor*'s Site Information', but if the *Contractor* has based his tender proposals on new site investigation work he will, with reason, want the results of the investigations included in the contract. How this is done will depend on how the site investigation work was organised.

If tenderers were left to their own devices, the *Employer* will want to satisfy himself that the site investigations were properly carried out before agreeing to any results being included as part of the contract. Once they are part of the contract they will in effect define the risk he is taking on ground conditions. If the *Employer* accepts that the site investigation was properly carried out and is genuinely representative, he could agree to adding the results to the Site Information defined in the Contract Data part one.

If the *Employer* carried out the site investigation work on behalf of the tenderers during the tender period, the results are simply included in the Site Information, and no change is necessary to any clause of the contract.

If the site investigation work is carried out as part of the contract, all that is necessary is a clear definition of the reference conditions, and confirmation that conditions outside the reference condition boundaries constitute a compensation event. It is sensible to define, in the contract, criteria for recognising that conditions found in the new investigation are outside the reference condition boundaries, so that, for example, one 'rogue' result does not outweigh five consistent results obtained earlier by the *Employer*.

EXPLANATORY NOTES

1 GENERAL

Core clauses

Actions **10**

10.1 This clause obliges the *Employer*, the *Contractor*, the *Project Manager* and the *Supervisor* to do everything which the contract states they do. It is the only clause which uses the future tense. For simplicity, everything else is in the present tense.

The requirement for the principal contributors to the operation of an ECC contract to do so in a spirit of mutual trust and co-operation was added on the recommendation of the Latham Report ('Constructing the Team'). This report, published in July 1994, was the final report of an investigation by Sir Michael Latham into procurement and contractual arrangements in the UK construction industry. The ECC takes account of all the recommendations of the Latham Report.

Where actions are permitted but not obligatory, the term 'may' is used.

Identified and defined **11**
terms 11.1 The main definitions used in the contract are given in Clause 11.2. Other definitions are given in optional clauses where they are specific to a particular Option. Capital initial letters are used in the ECC for the defined terms to distinguish them from undefined terms.

Any term that is identified in the Contract Data is written in italics; the *Project Manager* cannot change such identified terms.

A combination of these two systems is used when the details of a term in italics may need to be changed during the course of the contract – e.g. the Completion Date, Clause 11.2(3). The definition of the defined term (the Completion Date) includes a reference to the same term in italics (the *completion date*) but also refers to the possibility of changes 'in accordance with this contract'. This combination therefore provides

- a basis for tenders and the contract at the Contract Date, at which time the defined term is the same as the italicised term
- the flexibility to change the term, for example as the result of a compensation event, and
- the continual use of the defined term throughout the contract.

11.2
(1) The definition of the Accepted Programme is worded to allow for the two possible situations, where there may or may not be a programme referred to in the Contract Data part two. The *Employer* should make it clear to tenderers if he intends the tender programme to become the Accepted Programme by this means, and ideally any such tender programme should broadly comply with the requirements of Clause 31.2.

Note that the requirements of Clause 31.2 do not actually apply to any tender programme even if it does become the Accepted Programme. Clause 31.2 refers to programmes submitted by the *Contractor* for acceptance.

(2)   The Works Information should state what work is to be done before Completion; disputes can arise if this is not done clearly and unambiguously. This provides flexibility for the *Employer* to specify Completion at the level he requires and largely avoids the uncertainty associated with terms such as 'substantial completion' or 'partial completion'. Where normal practice is to equate Completion with absolute completion, as in some Middle Eastern countries, the Works Information will be written so that work must be free of Defects before Completion.

Note that Completion is a state, not a date; some people confuse the two. Completion may actually occur before, on or after the Completion Date.

(3)   The *completion date* stated in the Contract Data may be changed in various ways, for example as a consequence of a compensation event or of an agreement to accelerate.

(4)   Contracts come into existence by various means – sometimes by means of a counter-offer and its acceptance, sometimes after extended negotiations and discussions. The Contract Date is used to define the date when the contract comes into existence, regardless of the means by which this is achieved.

It is very important to establish and document the means by which the contract came into existence and the date on which it came into existence. If this is not done, there is a significant risk of later difficulties if a dispute about the contract arises. (See also earlier notes on 'Creating the contract'.)

(5)   The word 'Defect' has a restricted definition. It is intended to include unfinished or omitted parts of the *works*.

(6)   Issue of the Defects Certificate signifies the end of most of the obligations of the Parties. Uncorrected Defects listed in the Defects Certificate are dealt with using the procedure set out in Clause 45. The list should include unfinished or omitted parts of the *works*, implying that an inspection by the *Supervisor* is necessary prior to the *defects date*.

(7)   The definition of Equipment is broad and avoids using separate terms for items which are treated in the same way under the contract. It covers, for example, construction plant, vehicles, consumables, tools, temporary works, cabins, temporary access roads and other site facilities. The term 'Equipment' has been used where it has been customary to use 'plant' or 'constructional plant' in UK building and (until recently) civil engineering practice. This change is made so that the ECC can be used internationally and for other engineering work where it is customary for 'the plant' to mean part of the *works* to be provided.

Normally Equipment is eventually removed from the Site but there is provision in Clause 72 for the *Project Manager* to give approval for certain items to be left. For example, the *Contractor* may request that temporary piling should be left in, to save the cost of extraction. Also, the *Project Manager* may be content to permit 'sacrificial' formwork to be left in place.

(8)   The Fee includes all the costs of the *Contractor* that are not included in Defined Cost, together with his profit and any allowance for his risks (see Clause 52.1). The Fee is calculated by applying the *fee percentages* stated in the Contract Data part two to the relevant parts of the Defined Cost.

The Fee is used in assessing compensation events and, for Options C, D, E and F, in assessing amounts due to the *Contractor*.

(9)   Key Dates can be used on projects where two or more contractors are employed to carry out work on the same project under separate contracts with a common *Employer* and, usually, the same *Project Manager*. The overall project programme will usually require that the work being carried out by each of the contractors is dependent upon the actions of the others. The setting of Key Date(s) can be used by the *Project Manager* to ensure that the *Contractor* completes a defined activity or part of the *works* (which of itself is not a Section) to a precise programmed timescale and to achieve a stated Condition, so that the other contractors, or the *Employer*, can proceed with their work in accordance with the overall project programme.

A Key Date is different from a Sectional Completion Date (see Option X5) in that it does not require the completion of all of the work in a defined area of the site or the taking over of that area by the *Employer* once achieved. Further explanation of Sectional Completion is given in the explanatory notes for Option X5.

For each Key Date it is necessary to define what work has to be done by that date; the contract refers to this as the Condition. For example, the *Employer* on a project to construct a new industrial or water treatment facility may employ one contractor to construct the building and another to supply and install the plant inside. However, some of the plant may need to be placed on its foundations in the building before the outer skin of the building is complete because it may not be possible to install it afterwards. A Key Date can be set out in the Contract Data described as

condition to be met	*key date*
Foundations for the plant in the Press Room shall be complete and ready to allow the plant to be installed in its final position.	Week 27

Further examples of *conditions* and *key dates* could include the following.

- The *Contractor*'s design reaching a defined stage to enable information to be passed to Others so that their design can proceed.
- A wall being built to a certain level so that Others can start to fix their plant to it.
- The completion of some, but not all, of the *works* on a floor of a multi-storey building to a stage that will enable another contractor to start his work, which is to be carried out at the same time as the remainder of the *works* on that floor.

It is not necessary to use the Key Date provisions in the ECC. If the entries for completion of Key Dates in the Contract Data is left blank there will be no Key Dates in the contract.

Throughout the contract, Key Dates are managed in the same way as Completion (or Sectional Completion if Option X5 is used). They must be shown on all of the programmes that the *Contractor* produces – see Clause 31.2. They can be changed if they are affected by a compensation event. The *Project Manager* can change them (see Clause 14.3), but such change may, in itself, be a compensation event – see Clause 60.1(4). They are also subject to the acceleration quotation (Clause 36) and Early Warning (Clause 16) procedures.

(10) The defined term 'Others' provides a convenient means of reference to people and organisations not directly involved in the contract. However, there are instances where such a general term is not appropriate, e.g. in Clause 16.2. In these cases the term 'other people' is used to avoid any impression of a typing error which might have been given if 'others' were to be used without the capital initial.

(12) Items temporarily used in the construction but removed at or before Completion are excluded from Plant and Materials; they are Equipment.

(14) The Risk Register is a new addition to the third edition of the ECC, and develops one of the aims of the contract – that of encouraging good project management. It is a live document and will change during the progress of the work. Initially it will contain those risks identified by the *Employer* and the *Contractor* in parts one and two respectively of the Contract Data. Risks are then added to the Risk Register as part of the early warning process described in Clause 16, or removed because of actions taken by the Parties to avoid them or because they did not happen.

Large contracts already use risk registers or similar risk identification and management techniques. This contract now makes a Risk Register a necessary part of the contract management procedures of the Parties.

The first objective of the Risk Register is to identify the risks inherent in a project. Some of these risks are generic, and will apply to whatever work is carried out. An example is the risk of errors in pricing of the tender. Other risks will be specific to a particular operation. An example is the risk of foundation failure due to ground conditions being worse than expected.

The second objective of the Risk Register is to set out how the risks should be managed. It describes who will take what action to manage the risk or to minimise the likelihood of the risk event happening. The Risk Register will refer to other, more detailed documents setting out specific procedures to be implemented. These procedures will include the *Contractor*'s quality management system.

The third objective of the Risk Register is to identify the time and cost consequences to the Parties and Others if the risk event occurs. Whilst the Risk Register allocates the actions needed to manage the risk, the rest of the *conditions of contract* deal with the allocation of the cost and time consequences of that risk.

For contracts based on Options A or B, the allocation is straightforward – the total cost and time resulting from the event is borne by the *Contractor* unless it is covered by a compensation event or is an *Employer*'s risk listed in Clause 80.1. If it is covered by either of these, the total cost is borne by the *Employer* through the operation of the compensation event procedures.

For target contracts, Options C or D, if the risk is a compensation event or is an *Employer*'s risk listed in Clause 80.1, its cost and time implications are again borne by the *Employer*. If the event is not one of these, the costs will initially be borne by the *Employer* but will eventually be shared through the application of the *Contractor's* share mechanism in Clause 53. However, the definition of Disallowed Cost in Clause 11.2(25) should be noted. If a risk event results from a failure identified in this definition, the resulting cost will be disallowed, and the risk will be the *Contractor's*.

For cost reimbursable contracts, Options E or F, all of the risks will usually be borne by the *Employer* unless the event results from a failure identified in the definition of Disallowed Cost in Clause 11.2(25) or 11.2(26).

The key objective of the Risk Register is to apply pre-assessed and documented risk management procedures to specific, identified hazards. The information provided with the Risk Register, including the allowances made for risk, provide a much greater understanding of basic costs and the cost of risk transfer. This helps in both cost assessment of future work and budgetary management.

The *Employer* lists the risks that he wants to be included in the Risk Register in the Contract Data part one; the tenderer adds other risks in the Contract Data part two.

Following contract award, the Risk Register is updated and reviewed as part of the early warning process – see Clause 16.

(15) The *boundaries of the site* will normally be shown on a drawing which is identified in part one of the Contract Data.

(16) Site Information includes information about the Site and its surroundings. It is not specific to the work that is to be carried out on the Site; it is simply factual information. Guidance on assembling the Site Information is given under 'Preparing the tender documents'.

(17) This definition of a Subcontractor does not include a supplier to the *Contractor* except as stated in the clause. 'Labour-only' subcontractors are not Subcontractors under this definition; a designer, who provides the 'service' of designing all or parts of the *works* for the *Contractor*, is a Subcontractor.

(18)   Working Areas are important in respect of payments to the *Contractor* under Options C, D and E (see the Schedule of Cost Components), for assessing compensation events (see the Schedule of Cost Components and the Shorter Schedule of Cost Components) and in relation to Title (see Section 7). The *working areas* proposed by the *Contractor* in the Contract Data part two only become the Working Areas if they comply with this definition.

The *Contractor* may wish to extend the Working Areas to cover areas of land that he proposes to use temporarily for the purposes of the contract. Examples are a borrow pit or a compound that is outside the Site. The procedure for this is set out in Clause 15.

(19)   Works Information is information about the *works* to be provided. Detailed guidance on assembling the Works Information is given under 'Preparing the tender documents'. Works Information can be changed by the *Project Manager* during the course of the contract (Clause 14.3).

Communications 13

13.1   The phrase 'in a form which can be read, copied and recorded' includes a document sent by post, telex, cable, electronic mail, facsimile transmission, and on disk, magnetic tape or other electronic means.

13.3   These clauses establish the use of a *period for reply* wherever the term
& 13.4   (identified in the Contract Data part one) is used in the *conditions of contract*.

In some circumstances it may be appropriate to specify more than one *period for reply* in the Contract Data. The obvious example is for a response by the *Project Manager* to submissions of the *Contractor*'s design. Such specific cases should be described by reference to specific clauses of the contract, and it should be made clear that the 'general' period of reply applies to all other cases. Relying on Clause 13.5 for this purpose may not be sufficient, as the *Contractor* may not agree, and it is better for the *Contractor* to know how long the *Project Manager* will need to review design submissions when he is preparing his programme.

13.5   This clause provides for extending the *period for reply* by agreement. Where other periods for action are stated in the ECC, provisions for their extension (if any) are stated in the relevant clauses.

13.7   The requirement to notify information required by the contract separately is included to avoid important things being overlooked. For example, so that delays which could be avoided are not missed, submission of a revised programme which shows a delay does not count as an early warning of the delay. Requiring separate notices also makes it much easier to track the procedure following the issue of the notice.

Note that giving an early warning of a matter which has already been notified as a compensation event is not required (see Clause 16.1).

13.8   The ECC contains a number of examples of situations in which a *Project Manager* must either accept or reject a document which contains proposals submitted by the *Contractor*. The first example is in Clause 13.4. As Clause 13.8 says, the *Project Manager* has authority to withhold acceptance of a submission for any reason, although it is clearly not sensible for him to withhold acceptance for a reason which has no bearing on the interests of the *Employer*. However, some of these reasons may be quite outside the influence of the *Contractor* or may arise due to factors which the *Contractor* had no means of foreseeing. The mechanism described in Clause 13.8 is introduced to limit the *Contractor*'s risk in this situation. He does carry the risk of the *Project Manager* withholding acceptance for a reason stated in the contract. Withholding acceptance for any other reason is a compensation event (Clause 60.1(9)).

The *Project Manager* and **14**
the *Supervisor* **14.1** The *Project Manager* is the key person involved in the management of the contract from the *Employer*'s point of view. His duties and authority are described in the clauses of the contract. They are not summarised in a single clause.

It is assumed that the *Project Manager* will confer with the *Employer* as necessary in deciding which of various possible actions to take and in making other decisions which affect the outcome of the project as far as the *Employer* is concerned. For example, the *Project Manager* has full authority to arrange an acceleration of work, although the *Employer* would normally be vitally interested. The fact that the *Employer* is not often mentioned in the contract does not mean that the *Employer* has only a minor role. It does mean that, for the purposes of the contract, almost all dealings with the *Contractor* are handled by the *Project Manager*.

The *Project Manager* should advise the *Employer* whenever he sees fit, or when his conditions of engagement require, of any action which the *Project Manager* is considering. For example, the *Project Manager* may inform the *Employer* of acceptable quotations for compensation events, and also consult with him on which alternative quotation most suits the *Employer*'s requirements.

The *Contractor* will expect that all decisions which the contract envisages will be taken by the *Project Manager* will be taken by him within the time limits stated in the contract. In some organisations, this may require the *Project Manager* to pass on decisions to the *Contractor* which have in fact been taken by the *Employer*. This may happen, for example, when an *Employer* has not delegated the authority to make a particular type of decision to his *Project Manager*. This creates no difficulty provided that the internal arrangements between the *Employer* and the *Project Manager* enable the decisions to be made and communicated to the *Contractor* through the *Project Manager* within the contractual time limits.

The *Supervisor* will normally be appointed by the *Employer*. His main function is to check that work is carried out in compliance with the Works Information. This may include testing of materials and workmanship and observing tests which the *Contractor* carries out. He is also concerned with identifying and correcting Defects and, eventually, certifying the remaining Defects when he issues the Defects Certificate. His activities may have financial consequences, but he is not directly involved in financial matters. The actions of the *Project Manager* and *Supervisor* are independent of each other. There is no appeal from the *Supervisor* to the *Project Manager* where the actions of the *Supervisor* are questioned by the *Contractor*. If the *Contractor* is dissatisfied with an action of either the *Project Manager* or the *Supervisor*, his appeal is to the *Adjudicator*. (See also notes in 'Introduction'.)

14.2 On major contracts, it is normal for both the *Project Manager* and *Supervisor* to have staff to help them carry out their duties. This clause enables them to delegate specific authorities and duties under the contract to particular members of staff or other people. Before delegation is effective, the *Contractor* must first be notified. Notification to the *Contractor* should include details of the actions delegated and the person to whom they are delegated.

Delegation does not prevent the person who delegates from also acting himself. The *Project Manager* would normally advise the *Employer* and the *Supervisor*, as well as the *Contractor*, of any delegation of his actions, but this is entirely a matter for arrangement between these parties. In the same way the *Supervisor* would normally inform the *Project Manager* and the *Employer* of any delegation of his actions. A *Project Manager* will not normally delegate actions to the *Supervisor*, or the other way round. However, in very small contracts, where for example the *Supervisor* is absent for unavoidable reasons, it may be convenient for him to delegate his actions to the *Project Manager*.

14.3   The authority to change the Works Information belongs exclusively to the *Project Manager* and any person to whom he delegates this authority. Neither the *Employer* nor the *Supervisor* can change the Works Information. The *Adjudicator* cannot change the Works Information. The ECC does not limit the ordinary meaning of the word 'change' in relation to a change to the Works Information. Consequently, it includes additions to and deletions from the Works Information as well as alterations to it. If, for example, the *Project Manager* issues new information which he intends merely to clarify a previously issued drawing or specification clause this is as much a change to the Works Information as the issue of a new drawing which adds to the work which the *Contractor* has to do. Consequently, all such changes are potentially compensation events as set out in Clause 60.1(1).

Adding to the Working   **15**
Areas   15.1   The 'original' w*orking areas* are defined in Contract Data Part two. As his plans develop, the *Contractor* may find that he needs to add further areas as Working Areas, for example an additional borrow pit. This clause gives the *Project Manager* discretion to refuse acceptance, in that there are two reasons for not accepting the *Contractor*'s proposal, but he is not obliged to refuse.

Early warning   **16**
16.1   The purpose of this clause is to make binding the obligation to warn as soon as possible of anything which may affect the cost, timing of Completion or a Key Date, or the quality of the *works*. The sanction for failure by the *Contractor* to give early warning is to reduce the payment due to him for a related compensation event (Clause 63.5).

The *Project Manager* is motivated to give early warning in order to maximise the time available to consider the problem with the *Contractor* and thereby to increase the likelihood of finding the best solution to meet the *Employer*'s interests.

If an early warning is given by either the *Project Manager* or the *Contractor*, the *Project Manager* is required to make an addition to the Risk Register to cover the matter.

16.2   This clause authorises the *Project Manager* or the *Contractor* to call a risk reduction meeting at any time to discuss any problems or potential problems. These are matters that will be included in the Risk Register. As the Contract Data includes a list of risks that are to be included in the Risk Register, it would be sensible to call a risk reduction meeting at an early stage in the contract to discuss them. Then, as problems or potential problems are identified that give rise to early warnings, further meetings can be called to deal with these 'new' matters.

Examples of such problems are

- discovery of unexpected ground conditions,
- potential delay in the supply of crucial materials or plant,
- potential delay caused by the work of public utilities or other contractors,
- effects of bad weather,
- failure by a Subcontractor to perform, and
- design problems.

It may be agreed that other people should attend according to the particular circumstances. For example, Subcontractors, suppliers, public utilities, local authority representatives or the *Employer* himself may need to attend. (This is an example of where the defined term 'Others' would not have been appropriate.)

16.3 The intention of the requirement for the *Contractor* and *Project Manager* (and any other people attending the meeting) to co-operate is to ensure, as far as possible, that actions are taken and decisions made which avoid or mitigate the effects of identified risks on cost, quality and time.

Note that the intention of the meeting is to solve the problem. It is not to decide responsibility, or who will pay for actions taken; the relevant provisions of the contract will cover these aspects quite adequately.

16.4 It is useful for the *Project Manager* to record any decisions about actions to be taken, stating not only who will take them but also when action will be taken.

Ambiguities and inconsistencies **17**

17.1 This clause is intended to ensure that action is taken as soon as possible to deal with ambiguities and inconsistencies which are noticed in the contract documents. There is no stated precedence of documents. The *Project Manager* has the responsibility of instructing resolution of an ambiguity problem or an inconsistency in or between documents. An instruction to change the Works Information in order to resolve an ambiguity or inconsistency is a compensation event. Assessment is based on the 'contra proferentem' rule as expressed in Clause 63.8.

If an inconsistency becomes apparent between the Works Information provided by the *Employer* and a design which is part of the Works Information provided by the *Contractor* and included in part two of the Contract Data, the instruction would normally be to require the design to comply with the *Employer*'s Works Information. Such a change would not be a compensation event (Clause 60.1(1)).

Illegal and impossible requirements **18**

18.1 A change to the Works Information in order to resolve illegal or impossible requirements in the Works Information is a compensation event (Clause 60.1(1)).

Prevention **19**

19.1 This is in effect a 'force majeure' clause. It covers events that either stop the *Contractor* completing the *works* or make it impossible for him to complete on time, whatever measures he might take. No specific notification of such an event is required; it will have been notified under Clause 16, and it will be as a result of the consequent risk reduction meeting that the event is recognised as falling under the provisions of this Clause 19. Once it is so recognised, the *Project Manager* has authority to manage the consequences in the best interests of the *Employer,* and the event is a compensation event (60.1(19)). The event is therefore at the *Employer*'s risk for both time and cost.

A delay to planned Completion which can (as opposed to will) be recovered by acceleration, by increased resources, or by adjusting the programme does not stop the *Contractor* from completing on time. The *Contractor* must demonstrate that there is no reasonable means by which he can complete the *works* on time for the event to be recognised under the second bullet point.

In certain circumstances the event may lead to termination by the *Employer* – see Clause 91.7.

Main Option clauses

Identified and defined **11**
terms 11.2 All the main Option clauses in Section 1 are definitions concerning payment and cost. Guidance on these is included in the explanatory notes on Section 5.

2 THE *CONTRACTOR*'S MAIN RESPONSIBILITIES

This section sets out the *Contractor*'s main responsibilities. Other sections deal with particular responsibilities appropriate to the section heading.

Core clauses

Providing the Works **20**

20.1 This clause states the *Contractor*'s basic obligation. 'Provide the Works' is defined in Clause 11.2(13). The Works Information is defined in Clause 11.2(19). The Works Information provided by the *Employer* should state everything the *Contractor* is to do, including design work.

The *Contractor*'s design **21**

The ECC is suitable for use both in traditional civil engineering contracts, where all permanent work is designed by or on behalf of the *Employer* and the *Contractor*'s obligation is limited to constructing the *works*, and in package deal contracts, where the *Contractor* designs and builds the whole of the *works* in accordance with criteria specified by the *Employer*. Between these two limits, contracts will include some design done by the *Employer* and some by the *Contractor*. For instance, it is common for civil engineering and building works to be fully designed by or on behalf of the *Employer*, with mechanical and electrical plant designed by the *Contractor* to the performance requirements of the *Employer*.

Using Option F, the ECC is suitable for a design and management contract as well as for a design and construct contract.

21.1 Those parts of the *works* which the *Contractor* is required to design should be stated in the Works Information provided by the *Employer* and the interfaces with those parts of the *works* designed by the *Employer* identified. This may be done by stating 'everything except the following' or 'the following'. It is not recommended that parts of an element of work should be designed by different parties as this may confuse liability in the event of Defects occurring.

Where the *Contractor* is required to design a part of the *works*, the *Employer* should state in the Works Information the criteria to which he requires designs to conform. This may include details of the form, geometry and dimensions of the *works*, specifications, codes of practice, standards, reference to Site Information (provided by the *Employer)* and environmental criteria. (See earlier notes on 'Preparing the tender documents'.)

Where the *Contractor* is to carry out most of the design, similar criteria should be stated in the form of a performance specification. This will describe the characteristics, nature and performance of the finished work and should include any limitations which the *Employer* wishes to impose upon appearance, durability, operating and maintenance cost, etc.

Any change to the allocation of design responsibility or change or addition to the design criteria in the Works Information in part one of the Contract Data constitutes a change to the Works Information and is a compensation event.

21.2 The procedures for submission by the *Contractor* of design particulars and acceptance by the *Project Manager* are set out in this clause. The time limits are those stated in Clause 13. They are intended to encourage prompt action by the parties so that delay can be avoided and the whole process properly managed.

Two reasons for not accepting the *Contractor*'s design are stated. The *Project Manager* is not obliged to refuse acceptance of the *Contractor*'s design which does not comply with the Works Information but, if he does accept such design, he should change the Works Information accordingly. As stated in Clause 60.1(1), such a change to the Works Information may or may not be a compensation event (see explanatory notes on Clause 60.1(1)).

Sometimes the *Project Manager* will see in the design submitted by the *Contractor* characteristics which, if they had been foreseen, he would earlier have stated to have been unacceptable by including an appropriate constraint in the Works Information. In this situation, the *Project Manager* should add the constraint to the Works Information in order to justify his withholding of acceptance of the *Contractor*'s design. This change to the Works Information is a compensation event. This clause in the ECC ensures that the *Contractor* is protected from the risk of additional constraints on his design being introduced after his commitment to the Prices for the work has been made.

Clause 14.1 makes clear that, when the *Project Manager* accepts the *Contractor*'s design, there is no change of liability for the design. The *Employer* is thus placing reliance on the design skill of the *Contractor*.

The final sentence is intended to prevent abortive work which would result if the *Contractor* began to manufacture or construct to a design which had not been accepted.

21.3   It is important that submissions by the *Contractor* are in packages which are capable of being properly assessed. For instance, a foundation design cannot be properly assessed without some details of the superstructure and any Plant to be supported.

Design of Equipment 23

23.1   This clause allows the *Project Manager* to accept the *Contractor*'s design of Equipment without affecting the *Contractor*'s responsibilities (Clause 14.1). The *Contractor* is still liable if, after having made the Equipment to details which have been accepted, it fails because it did not comply with the Works Information. The clause gives three criteria for design of the Equipment. Failure to comply gives the *Project Manager* the right, but not the obligation, to decline to accept the design.

Unlike Clause 21.2, which provides that the *Contractor* should not proceed until the *Project Manager* has accepted the *Contractor*'s design of the *works*, there is no restraint on the *Contractor* proceeding even if the design of an item of Equipment has not been accepted.

The *Contractor* can proceed even though he has not obtained acceptance of his design of Equipment, which includes temporary works. The *Project Manager* should seek details of temporary works well in advance of when the work is going to be done (prompted by what he sees on the *Contractor*'s programme) so that he can register any dissatisfaction with the proposals in good time. However, responsibility for producing Equipment generally (including temporary works) that permits the *works* themselves to be completed properly lies with the *Contractor*.

People 24

24.1   This clause gives reasons for not accepting a proposed replacement for a key person. It does not preclude the *Project Manager* accepting a person with qualifications or experience which are inferior to the listed person, if he is satisfied that such a person will be suitable for the position.

24.2 This clause provides the authority for the *Project Manager*, on behalf of the *Employer*, to have a *Contractor*'s employee removed from work on the contract. Possible reasons for asserting this authority include

- security,
- health and safety (communicable diseases), and
- disorderly behaviour prejudicing the *Employer*'s operations.

However, the *Project Manager* may do it for any reason, provided he states what it is.

Working with the *Employer* 25
and Others 25.1 On many projects there are several contractors and other organisations. These may include public utilities who are to divert their services or provide new services and plant. Sometimes a public utility employs its own contractor but the utility supervises the work. The duty of the *Contractor* to co-operate with Others has been expressed in general terms only as the detailed requirements will depend on the particular project and Site and should be fully described and explained in the Works Information. Failure to do so may lead to a compensation event (e.g. Clause 60.1(5)).

The *Contractor* is not responsible for the failure of Others to carry out their work in accordance with the Works Information unless the failure is caused by the *Contractor* not co-operating. The exchange of information on health and safety matters is particularly important in order to comply with the law as well as with the contract, see notes on Clause 27.4.

25.2 Where more than one contractor has access to the Site, it is important that the interfaces are defined in the Works Information. Any services to be provided by one contractor to another, or by or to the *Employer*, should also be stated. Responsibility for the provision and maintenance of facilities should also be stated. Examples of these facilities are

- access roads,
- scaffolding,
- cranes and hoists,
- welfare,
- security arrangements,
- storage,
- power supplies,
- water,
- compressed air, and
- telephone.

The interface between the contractors and other bodies is often complex. It is important that this work is planned and programmed as far as possible before the start of the contract. The start dates for work should be agreed together with details of the work, its likely duration and facilities required to be provided by and for the *Contractor*. Details of the obligations of the parties at each interface and the timing and programming arrangements should be agreed. This information may conveniently be provided in the form of interface schedules in the Works Information to ensure that arrangements in the different contracts are 'back-to-back'. It should also be stated which party is to supply and maintain access (e.g. scaffolding, lifting equipment for plant), resources (for testing, etc.) and other services (such as power supply and water supply).

If precise dates are not available, approximate dates should be given in the Works Information. The *Contractor* should then be required to meet the other parties soon after the *starting date*, agree detailed programmes with them and incorporate the information in his own programme.

In addition, the health and safety requirements, with which each contractor is required to comply, should be stated in the Works Information. This is particularly important for sites occupied by several contractors (see explanatory notes on Clause 27.4).

Failure by the *Employer* to provide the services and other things stated in the Works Information is a compensation event under Clause 60.1(3). Failure by the *Contractor* to provide the services and other things stated in the Works Information results in his having to pay any cost incurred by the *Employer* under Clause 25.2.

'Providing services and other things' is not to be confused with the *Employer*'s use of the *works*. The Works Information should include details of the services and other things which the *Employer* requires during the construction operations. This particularly applies where the *Contractor* is required to work in an area where the *Employer* needs to continue working, or when he requires an existing facility to be maintained. For example, in road construction projects, traffic must continue to flow, either on temporary diversions or on the partially constructed *works*. Details of the programming and how the *Contractor* provides for this traffic are usually left to the *Contractor*. In complex traffic management schemes, it may be necessary for the *Employer* to prepare full details in advance and include these in the Works Information.

25.3   See explanatory notes on Clauses 11.2(9) and 31.2. This clause establishes a procedure for the *Employer* to recover from the *Contractor* any additional costs he incurs due to the *Contractor* failing to meet the Condition required by the Key Date.

Subcontracting 26

26.1   These clauses provide that the *Contractor* may subcontract parts of the *works*,
26.2   provided the Project *Manager* accepts the proposed Subcontractors. In the case of proposals for subcontracts for small amounts of technically simple work, acceptance by the *Project Manager* may be a formality.

No provision is included in the ECC for nomination of Subcontractors. This is because of the legal and practical problems of accountability which frequently ensue. The principle of the ECC is that the *Contractor* is fully responsible for every aspect of managing the work he has contracted for (hence Clause 26.1). Nominating Subcontractors conflicts with this principle and causes many practical problems. Alternatives to nominating Subcontractors whilst achieving similar objectives are

(a)   making the *Contractor* responsible for all work; he may then subcontract parts and the *Project Manager* retains some control over the identity of the Subcontractors provided any withholding of acceptance is for the reason stated,

(b)   providing for separate contracts, with the *Project Manager* managing the time and physical interfaces between them,

(c)   including lists of acceptable Subcontractors for particular tasks in the Works Information.

Where national or international law requires, the Works Information should include a statement of award criteria for subcontracts.

Acceptance of a Subcontractor cannot be withdrawn later, providing his appointment complies with these clauses.

26.3   The NEC Engineering and Construction Subcontract (or the NEC Professional Services Contract for design work) is expected to be used as recommended in the Latham Report (July 1994). The NEC Engineering and Construction Short Subcontract is also available for straightforward, low risk subcontracts. However, in overseas contracts or where the requirements of a particular industry make the NEC subcontracts inappropriate, the *Project Manager* may accept other subcontract conditions being used (see also explanatory notes on Clauses 13.8 and 60.1(9)).

Other responsibilities 27

27.1   This clause requires the *Contractor* to obtain the requisite approvals for his design from planning authorities, nuclear inspectorates and Others who may have the duty or authority to approve his design. The contract is silent about the *Contractor* obtaining approval from outside bodies to other aspects of his work such as road closures or access for major items of Equipment.

27.2   It is important that the *Project Manager*, Others notified by the *Project Manager* and the *Supervisor* have the right to visit places where work is being carried out. This includes right of access to suppliers' and Subcontractors' premises to permit them to inspect and test work as necessary and to check progress.

27.3   Various clauses in the contract give the *Project Manager* and the *Supervisor* authority to issue instructions to the *Contractor*. It is important that these instructions are given within the limits and for the reasons expressly stated. If, for any reason, the *Contractor* disagrees with an instruction, his remedy is not to refuse to obey the instruction, but to follow the dispute resolution procedure chosen for the contract (Option W1 or Option W2).

27.4   In many countries there are laws which place considerable responsibilities upon employers, employees and others in relation to health and safety. In most European countries there is considerable legislation relating to health and safety on construction sites. This legislation is regularly being increased in scope. Generally, the sanctions for non-compliance are criminal in nature as opposed to civil. It is not appropriate or necessary to reproduce or to summarise this legislation in contract documents. The various parties each have their obligations under statute and the general law.

It is necessary, however, to include in the contract any particular requirements which the *Employer* has. These requirements are stated in the Works Information since they affect how the *Contractor* is to Provide the Works and are in parallel with statutory obligations. These requirements may include such matters as

- the safety regulations of the factory within which the Site is located,
- a health and safety plan for the whole Site and the project,
- submission of safety policies for information, and
- which party is responsible for maintaining areas used by several contractors in a safe condition.

In 1995, the Construction (Design and Management) Regulations 1994 came in to force in the United Kingdom. They require construction projects to adopt a regime of health and safety management which includes many matters which might formerly have been covered by specific *Employer*'s requirements. The principal contractor and the planning supervisor should be identified in the Works Information.

Main Option clauses

Options C, D, E and F

20

20.3   These clauses illustrate the collaborative nature of these main Options
20.4

Subcontracting 26.4   See explanatory notes on Clause 26.3 for available NEC Subcontracts. This clause gives the *Project Manager* more information about a proposed subcontract than is available under Options A and B, but it does not permit the *Project Manager* to control or influence the choice of subcontractor.

When Option C, D or E is used in a partnering arrangement it is common for the *Project Manager* to want more influence over the selection of a subcontractor. This can be achieved by setting down the processes to be followed in an Option Z clause.

Especially under Option F, detailed procurement procedures should be stated clearly, preferably in a Z clause. These should include such matters as

- minimum number of competitive tenders,
- criteria on how a subcontractor is appointed, and
- involvement of the *Project Manager* in the procurement process and acceptance of Subcontractors.

Option F: Management contract

Providing the Works **20**

20.2   In a management contract, the core clauses and this clause state how the *Contractor* is to Provide the Works by identifying what he is to do himself and what he is to subcontract.

The effects are shown in the table below. This also shows how the *Contractor* is paid by relating the different categories of work to the Defined Cost, the Fee and the prices stated in the Contract Data.

Providing the Works

Contractor does not subcontract		*Contractor* must subcontract
Management of • the *Contractor*'s design • provision of Site services • construction and installation of the *works*	Work stated in Contract Data part two to be done by the *Contractor*	• The *Contractor*'s design • Provision of Site services • Construction and installation of the works except work which the Contract Data states he will do himself
Covered by the Fee	Prices stated in the Contract Data	Included in Defined Cost

It is important that tenderers for an Option F management contract state and price any work the *Contractor* would want to do himself in the Contract Data part two. If this is not done, the work would have to be subcontracted or its price covered by the Fee.

20.5   This clause provides a co-operative procedure to deal with compensation events affecting the work stated in the Contract Data that the *Contractor* is to do himself.

3 TIME

Core clauses

Starting, Completion and Key Dates	30	The period of time within which the *Contractor* is required to Provide the Works is not stated. Instead, the *starting date* and the *completion date* are given in the Contract Data. The *starting date* is the date when the *Contractor* can start work, but not on Site (see Clause 30.1). The *starting date* is also used to initiate the fixing of some dates and intervals throughout a contract, e.g. payment assessment dates (Clause 50.1) and interval for revised programmes (Clause 32.2). Both *starting date* and *completion date* may be adjusted by agreement before the Contract Date.

For many contracts, the period between the *starting* date and the *completion date* is decided by the *Employer*, enabling the *completion date* to be inserted in the Contract Data before inviting tenders.

Alternatively, the *completion date* may be decided by the tenderers and submitted as part of their offers. If this is done, *Employers* should make clear how tenders are to be assessed, indicating the value to be placed on an early *completion date*.

Sometimes, the *completion date* is decided by the *Employer* but alternative tenders are also invited on the basis of an earlier tendered *completion date*. Again in such a case, the basis of assessing tenders should be made clear to the tenderers.

It is essential for *completion dates* to be stated (by one of the above methods) in a construction contract. Even if the extent of the work is uncertain, which may be the case in a cost reimbursable contract, a time should be stated based on a stated assumed amount of work. If this is not done, extension of time and delay damages provisions cannot be applied.

30.1 The *Contractor* cannot start work on Site until the first *access date*. The *access dates* are stated in the Contract Data. In contracts for the manufacture and installation of plant, or when the *Contractor* has to do significant pre-planning or design, the first *access date* may be some time after the *starting date*.

30.2 The *Project Manager* is responsible for certifying Completion, as defined in Clause 11.2(2), within one week of Completion. Normally, the *Contractor* will ask for the certificate as soon as he considers he is entitled to it, but such a request is not essential.

30.3 See notes on Clauses 11.2(9), 25.3 and 31.2.

The programme 31

31.1 Provision is made in the Contract Data for a programme either to be identified in the Contract Data part two at the Contract Date or to be submitted by the *Contractor* within a period stated in the Contract Data part one.

The programme is an important document for administering the contract. It enables the *Project Manager* and *Contractor* to monitor progress and to assess the time effects of compensation events, including changes to the Completion Date.

Employers may wish to have programmes submitted with tenders in order to judge whether a tenderer has fully understood his obligations and whether he is likely to be able to carry out the work within the stated time, using the methods and resources he proposes. Any doubts on these matters can then be resolved after submission of tenders.

Acceptance of a programme, unlike acceptance of the *Contractor*'s design, is not a condition precedent to the *Contractor* proceeding with the work. Failure to accept a revised programme does not require the *Contractor* to stop work.

31.2 This clause lists the information which the *Contractor* is required to show on each programme submitted for acceptance. The following notes are broadly in the same order as the bullets in the clause.

- The dates stated in the Contract Data or changed in accordance with the contract (see explanatory notes on Clauses 11.2(3), 11.2(9), 30 and 33).
- The *Contractor*'s updated planned Completion (and Sectional Completion if Option X5 is used) as the work progresses.
- The order and timing of the *Contractor*'s own work, updated (ref. Clause 32.1).
- The work of the *Employer* and Others. The reference to 'last agreed' allows for changes to be made to the interfaces, in accordance with the contract.
- The dates when the *Contractor* plans to complete work for which Key Dates apply (see explanatory notes on Clause 11.2(9)) and work needed to allow the *Employer* and Others to do their work.
- Separate references to 'float' and to 'time risk allowances' are included in Clause 31.2. It is important that they are each clearly identifiable on the programme.

The *Contractor*'s time risk allowances are to be shown on his programme as allowances attached to the duration of each activity or to the duration of parts of the *works*. These allowances are owned by the *Contractor* as part of his realistic planning to cover his risks. They should be either clearly identified as such in the programme or included in the time periods allocated to specific activities. It follows that they should be retained in the assessment of any delay to planned Completion due to the effect of a compensation event.

Float is any spare time within the programme after the time risk allowances have been included. It is normally available to accommodate the time effects of a compensation event in order to mitigate or avoid any delay to planned Completion. However, in accordance with Clause 63.3, float attached to the whole programme (i.e. any float between planned Completion and the Completion Date) is not available. Any delay to planned Completion due to a compensation event therefore results in the same delay to the Completion Date. (See further explanatory notes on Clause 63.3.)

It is important that the time risk allowances included by the *Contractor* in a programme submitted for acceptance are realistic. If they are not, the *Project Manager* may refer to the third bullet of Clause 31.3 and refuse acceptance.

- The provision for health and safety matters should allow for any statutory procedures, as well as those specifically mentioned in the Works Information.
- The programme is to show the dates when the *Contractor* will need access and other things to be provided to him by the *Employer* and also information from Others.
- The penultimate bullet of Clause 31.2 covers the general information about resources the *Contractor* plans to use for each operation. In the early stages of the contract the *Contractor*'s statement will probably lack detail and reflect the methods and Equipment proposed in his tender. As the work progresses, the statement may be revised to show more detail and any changes he proposes for acceptance by the *Project Manager* (see explanatory notes on Clause 32).

- The *Employer* should ensure that the Works Information states the operations for which he requires detailed method statements. This requirement should be limited to operations where the method of construction and the design of the Equipment to be used are crucial if the design of the *works* is not to be put at undue risk. Where there is a large amount of *Contractor* design, it may be appropriate for the Works Information to require an increasing amount of detail to be shown on the programme as the design is developed.

31.3 This clause lists reasons why a *Project Manager* may decide not to accept a programme or a revised programme. Any failure by the *Project Manager* to accept a programme for reasons other than those noted is a compensation event (Clause 60.1(9)). The *Project Manager* is required to respond within two weeks, but if the reply is non-acceptance the *Contractor* is required to re-submit, within the *period for reply.*

Revising the programme 32

32.1 This clause lists the matters which are to be shown on a revised programme. It should record the actual progress achieved on each operation and the reprogramming of future operations. It should also show the effects of implemented compensation events. If a compensation event affects the timing of future operations, the consequent alterations to the programme are to be submitted as part of the *Contractor*'s quotation (Clause 62.2). The revised programme should also show proposals for dealing with delays, Defects and any changes the *Contractor* wishes to make.

Failure by the *Contractor* to submit revised programmes is of considerable disadvantage to the *Contractor* in that if a compensation event occurs, the *Project Manager* may assess it entirely on the basis of his own judgement. Thus it is in the *Contractor*'s interests to keep the programme up to date and maintain the existence of an Accepted Programme (Clause 64.2).

32.2 The *Project Manager* should note, in reviewing a submitted revised programme, any changes to the dates by which the *Employer* is required to provide information, facilities, possession, etc. He should be prepared to accept a programme with earlier dates if this is acceptable to the *Employer*. After acceptance, any subsequent failure by the *Employer* to meet these earlier dates is a compensation event.

**Access to and use of 33
the Site** 33.1 The dates on which the *Contractor* may have access to the various parts of the Site are stated in the Contract Data. In many cases it may be possible to give access to the whole Site on the *starting date*. In other cases, particularly where there are several contractors on the Site, this may not be possible. The *Contractor* must then programme his activities according to the dates when he can have access.

The *Contractor* may not require access on the dates stated in the Contract Data, in which case he should show on his programme the later dates. These then supersede those in the Contract Data and become obligatory on the *Employer*.

**Instructions to stop or not 34
to start work** 34.1 This clause gives the *Project Manager* authority to control the stopping and re-starting of work for any reason, for example where there is risk of injury to people or damage to property. An instruction given constitutes a compensation event (Clause 60.1(4)), but if it arises from a fault of the *Contractor*, the Prices, Completion Date and Key Dates are not changed (Clauses 61.1 and 61.4). In certain circumstances, if the *Project Manager* fails to instruct the re-start of work within thirteen weeks of instructing work to stop, either Party may be entitled to terminate the contract under Clause 91.6.

Take over **35**

35.1   The *Employer* may have good reasons for not wishing to take over the *works* before the Completion Date. If so, this should be stated in the Contract Data. For example, the work in this contract may be part of a larger scheme such that there is no advantage to the *Employer* in its early completion. If the Contract Data is silent on this, the *Employer* is required to take over the *works* within two weeks of Completion.

If Option X5 is included in the contract and the *works* are divided into *sections*, Completion of a *section* results in the *Employer* having to take over the *section* within two weeks of its Completion.

35.2   Under this clause, if the *Employer* uses part of the *works* before Completion has been certified, he takes over that part on the date that he uses it and a compensation event occurs unless the take over is for a reason stated in the Works Information or to suit the *Contractor*'s method of working (see explanatory notes on Clause 60.1(15)). The *Employer* is then responsible for providing access so that the *Contractor* can correct Defects, which will include completing outstanding work (Clause 43.4).

Acceleration **36**

Acceleration means bringing the Completion Date or a Key Date forward. This differs from usage in many contracts where 'acceleration' means speeding up the work to ensure that the Completion Date or Key Date is achieved. If the *Project Manager* is concerned that delay which has already occurred may result in the Completion Date or a Key Date not being achieved, he can instruct the *Contractor* to produce a revised programme under Clause 32.1 showing how he intends to recover the time he has lost.

36.1
36.2   These clauses allow the *Project Manager* (often at the request of the *Employer*) to obtain a quotation for acceleration from the *Contractor*. There is no remedy if it is not produced or if the *Contractor*'s quotation is unacceptable. Acceleration cannot be imposed on the *Contractor* without his agreement.

An *Employer* who foresees the possibility of requiring acceleration should consider using Options C, D or E when deciding contract strategy, since acceleration agreements are more likely to be achieved under these Options than under Options A or B.

Main Option clauses

Options A and C

The programme   31

31.4   The activities on the Activity Schedule and the operations on the programme should be compatible in order to make assessment of compensation events and financial forecasting easier. However, the programme may contain more operations than the Activity Schedule has activities.

It is also possible that the Activity Schedule contains more activities than the number of operations in the programme. There should always be correlation between the programme and the Activity Schedule, whether the Accepted Programme is in the Contract Data (i.e. as part of an accepted tender) or prepared after the Contract Date. This correlation should be kept up to date as the job proceeds. Correlation is best achieved by adding to the Activity Schedule the relevant programme operation references.

Example of good correlation: each activity is made up of whole operations or part of one operation.

Activity number	Activity description	Price £	Programme operation
1	Excavate for west abutment	20,000	Part of 23
2	Excavate for central pier	18,000	24
3	Excavate for east abutment	23,000	Part of 23

Example of poor correlation: to be avoided.

Activity number	Activity description	Price £	Programme operation
6	Shuttering for west abutment	15,000	Part of 28 and part of 29
7	Shuttering for central pier	19,000	26 and part of 31
8	Shuttering for east abutment	17,000	27, 32 and part of 33

Options A, B, C and D

Acceleration   36

36.3   This clause states the actions to be taken by the *Project Manager* when he has accepted a quotation for an acceleration. The actions are the same as when the *Project Manager* implements a compensation event (Clause 65.4).

Options E and F

Acceleration   36

36.4   This clause states the actions to be taken by the *Project Manager* when he has accepted a quotation for an acceleration. The actions are the same as when the *Project Manager* implements a compensation event (Clause 65.3).

4 TESTING AND DEFECTS

Core clauses

The *Contractor*'s responsibility for quality is part of his duty to Provide the Works (Clause 20.1) as defined in Clause 11.2(13).

The quality standards to be achieved by the *Contractor* should be specified in the Works Information in part one of the Contract Data. These standards provide the basis on which the existence of a Defect is judged (Clause 11.2(5)). The *Supervisor* acts on the *Employer*'s behalf to check the *Contractor*'s attainment of the specified standards.

Quality systems

If quality systems are required in a project, they should be initiated by the *Employer* at an early stage, such as at the early design stages.

Requirements in the ECC for quality systems can be accommodated in two ways

(a) The *Employer* specifies requirements for quality management procedures in the Works Information in part one of the Contract Data.

(b) The *Employer* requires the *Contractor* to provide details of his quality plan for inclusion in the Works Information at the Contract Date.

Tests and inspections 40

40.1 Clause 40 does not apply to tests and inspections done by the *Contractor* at his own discretion and for his own purposes.

40.2 Tests should be specified in the Works Information with respect to

- the nature of the tests,
- when they are to be done,
- where they are to be done,
- who does the test,
- who provides materials, facilities and samples,
- their objectives and procedures, and
- whether or not payment or authorisation to proceed to the next stage of the work depends on the test results.

Additional tests may be instructed by the *Project Manager* by changing the Works Information. This is a compensation event under Clause 60.1(1) unless the test is either required to check for a Defect and one is found (Clause 60.1(10)) or it is a repeat test. Such instructions should specify details of the test.

When tests are to be done

Significant stages include the following.

- Before payment for or marking of Equipment or Plant and Materials (Clause 71.1).
- Before delivery to the Working Areas (Clause 41.1).
- Before Completion. The Works Information should state which tests have to be passed before Completion.
- Before Key Dates or dates shown on the Accepted Programme for the start of work by the *Employer* or Others. The Works Information should state the tests to be passed before these dates.

- After take over but before the *defects date*. Tests required during this period will usually be part of the *Employer*'s commissioning. In the case of process plants, they may involve production materials which the *Employer* may need to have under his direct control. Such tests may be carried out by the *Supervisor* on the *Employer*'s behalf or by the *Contractor*. It is possible that the completed parts of the *works* may be put into operation by the *Employer* before completing his own tests. A 'sunset' clause (40.5) is included to avoid the possibility of payments conditional on the successful completion of a *Supervisor*'s test being withheld if the test has not been carried out by the *defects date*. This provision does not apply to tests which have to be repeated due to discovery of a Defect.

Failure by the *Supervisor* to carry out his tests promptly is a compensation event (Clause 60.1(11)) if it causes unnecessary delay to the *Contractor*.

Where tests are to be done

The Works Information should state the location of each test if it is not to be carried out within the Working Areas. Items which may come into this category include heavy structural units, mechanical and electrical plant, computer and other proprietary equipment.

Who does the test

The Works Information should specify who is responsible for carrying out each test or for arranging for it to be carried out. The choice will be between the following.

- The *Contractor*, including his Subcontractors and suppliers. Where the *Contractor* is to arrange for a test to be carried out by an independent or public authority, the Works Information should include the name of the authority, the tests and the form in which the results are to be supplied.
- The *Supervisor*.

Who provides materials, facilities and samples

The Works Information should state who provides the materials and apparatus necessary for each test. The required items may include the following.

- Samples of materials to be tested. These are normally provided by the *Contractor*, his Subcontractors or suppliers.
- Testing apparatus, test loads, measuring instruments. These could be provided by the *Employer*, the *Supervisor* or the *Contractor* (including his Subcontractors or suppliers) or hired from an independent or public authority.
- Testing facilities such as a Site laboratory (normally provided by the *Contractor* but sometimes by the *Employer*) or laboratories off-Site (normally those of an independent company or authority).
- Services for the tests (water, electricity, air, steam, etc.) which are

  - off-Site – normally provided by the testing authority being used,
  - on-Site, before take over – normally provided by the *Contractor* from the services available on Site but sometimes augmented by the *Employer* when special services are required, or
  - on-Site, after take over – normally provided by the *Employer*.

- Materials for use in the tests (including performance tests) – normally provided by the *Employer* or by a specialist Subcontractor or supplier.
- Fuel for the tests (gas, coal, oil, etc.) – normally provided by the *Employer*
- Provision and disposal of production materials – normally provided or disposed of by the *Employer*.

Objectives, procedures, etc.	The objectives, procedures and the standards to be satisfied should be specified in the Works Information. Types of tests may include the following.

- Checking setting out, line, level, verticality.
- Measuring movements, settlement and soil characteristics in earthworks.
- Testing the properties of materials to be incorporated in the works for strength, durability, appearance, brittleness, flexibility, corrosion resistance, etc.
- Testing the structural, mechanical or pressure resisting strength of Plant, piping systems, structures or other parts of the works.
- Testing the performance, accuracy and reliability of control systems and associated instruments and servo-mechanisms incorporated in the works.
- Testing the reliability, safety and effectiveness of electrical, mechanical and other systems incorporated in the works.
- Testing the performance of the works including the performance of items of Plant to prove that they perform as specified in the Works Information.

40.3   This clause deals with four matters

- the procedure for notifying when testing is to be done,
- the requirement to notify test results,
- the timing of notifying the *Supervisor* of testing or inspection, and
- the right of the *Supervisor* to observe the *Contractor*'s tests.

The *Contractor* and *Supervisor* are each required to give the other advance notice of tests which each is to carry out. This enables both parties to be fully informed and to take any action they wish to take. If, for example, testing reveals that some work does not comply with the Works Information, early discussion of the consequences is likely to be required. Notification of tests and their results is required before further testing or inspection is rendered impossible or impracticable. For example, the results of a drain test should be notified before the drain is covered up, or the result of a test of reinforcing steel should be notified before concrete is placed around the reinforcement. Failure by the *Contractor* to notify the *Supervisor* of a test or inspection may deprive the *Contractor* of compensation for a search, even if no Defect is found (Clause 60.1(10)).

40.4   A Defect is defined in Clause 11.2(5). Any repeat test or inspection of work after a Defect has been corrected is not a compensation event.

A Defect may make it impossible to reconstruct the work affected in accordance with the Works Information. For example, piles which have been installed outside the specified tolerances may have disturbed the original ground such that the construction of the foundation as shown on the drawings has become impossible. The early warning procedure (Clause 16) requires early discussion of the matter. Possible solutions include changing the Works Information after redesign or accepting the Defect (Clause 44).

40.5   Under this clause, the *Supervisor* is required to carry out testing and inspection for which he is responsible so that unnecessary delay to the work is avoided. If unnecessary delay occurs a compensation event results (Clause 60.1(11)). Some payments to the *Contractor* may be conditional upon doing particular tests to show that the work has been carried out satisfactorily. If the *Supervisor* causes unnecessary delay, such payments may become due after the *defects date* whether or not the tests are carried out.

40.6   If a test has to be repeated following the discovery of a Defect, the *Contractor* pays the *Project Manager*'s assessment of the cost incurred by the *Employer*. If the cost reimbursable Options C, D or E are used, the *Project Manager*'s assessment does not include any costs the *Contractor* incurs for the repeat test (Clause 40.7).

Performance testing of
Process Plant

To prove that process Plant meets reliability, performance and other parameters, it is often necessary to test Plant after take over when regular operating services are available and full loads can be applied. For some processes long term 'soak' tests can be required.

The ECC test and inspection provisions allow for any combination of tests to be carried out before and after take over and/or Completion. There is therefore no need to have separate clauses in the *conditions of contract* (or add Z clauses) to deal with different types of test.

Many combinations of tests may be required for process Plant and it is not practical for the *conditions of contract* to prescribe particular tests. The *Employer* must state in the Works Information what tests are required (see notes on Clause 40.2), in a similar way to drafting a detailed traditional specification.

For a typical ECC contracted process Plant the testing regime would be as follows.

- **Manufacture**
  During manufacture various tests would be carried out in the factory. If the Works Information identifies specific tests to be carried out before delivery, they must be passed before the Plant is brought to the Working Areas (Clause 41.1).

- **Erection on site**
  Following erection on site, static alignment, electrical and mechanical and basic process automation tests stated in the Works Information will be performed (Clause 40).

  - If the Plant passes the tests and all other work required to achieve Completion is done, then take over may proceed.
  - If the Plant fails then a Defect exists and is corrected (Clause 43).

- **After take over**
  After take over, performance tests are carried out (also under Clause 40). The *Employer* and *Contractor* provide facilities, etc. (this would often include the services of operations staff) as stated in the Works Information (Clause 40.2).

  - If the Plant passes, the *Contractor* has met his obligations in this respect.
  - If Option X17 (low performance damages) is used and the performance is low, but within the levels stated in the Contract Data, low performance damages are paid by the *Contractor*.
  - If the performance is low and either X17 has not been used, or the failure is outside the limits of X17, a Defect exists and is corrected (Clause 44).
  - If the *Employer* is willing to accept the Defect, a price reduction may be agreed (Clause 44).
  - If the *Employer* is unwilling to accept the Defect and the *Contractor* cannot correct it, the *Project Manager* assesses the cost of having the Defect corrected by Others, which is paid by the *Contractor* (Clause 45.1).

It is useful to include in the Works Information a schedule tabulating details of the tests to be done at different stages of the *works* with cross-references to the relevant sections of the Works Information containing the detailed procedures.

Testing and inspection **41**
before delivery **41.1**

The purpose of this clause is to avoid expense in having to transport Plant and Materials back to the place of manufacture if testing and inspection reveal Defects.

Searching for and 42
notifying Defects 42.1   The *Contractor* is responsible for correcting a Defect as defined in Clause 11.2(5). A fault in a design provided by the *Employer* is not a Defect.

If a search is instructed and a defect is found which is due to a fault in the *Employer*'s design (i.e. no Defect as defined is found), the instruction to search is a compensation event (Clause 60.1(10)) and responsibility for further action belongs to the *Project Manager*. He may decide to change the design and instruct the *Contractor* accordingly. This would constitute a change to the Works Information, which would be a further compensation event (Clause 60.1(1)).

If the defect is due to non-compliance with the Works Information, it is a Defect and does not result in a compensation event. It is then the *Contractor*'s responsibility to correct the Defect so that the work complies with the Works Information.

The clause also includes extra tests and inspections not specified in the Works Information within the meaning of 'searching'. Whether or not such tests are compensation events is determined using Clause 60.1(10).

42.2   The intention of this clause is to enable Defects to be identified as soon as possible so that they can be dealt with promptly.

The periods for the notification and correction of Defects are illustrated in Figure 3.

The *defects date* is defined in the Contract Data as a date which is a stated period of time after Completion. Normal practice for most civil engineering and construction contracts in the United Kingdom would be a period of 12 months. For process plant, longer periods, commonly 3 years but up to 7 or even 10 years in special circumstances, may be appropriate.

Defects may be notified for correction by the *Contractor* at any time before the *defects date*. The d*efects date* is the earliest date when the *Contractor* ceases to be liable under the contract for the correction of Defects. However, the *Contractor*'s liability to correct Defects under the contract may continue after the *defects date* for the *defect correction period* if a Defect is notified just before the *defects date* (see Figure 3).

The *Supervisor*, *Project Manager* or *Employer* may inform the *Contractor* of Defects after the *defects date* but the *Contractor*'s responsibility for them may be limited according to the law governing the contract or by the operation of Option X18, if used.

Correcting Defects 43
43.1   The *Contractor* is responsible for correcting all Defects, whether notified or not.

Before completion, the *Contractor* is responsible for correcting all Defects which would prevent him fulfilling his obligation to Provide the Works in accordance with the Works Information (Clause 20.1). He therefore needs to correct Defects in time to avoid delaying

- Completion, as defined in Clause 11.2(2),
- if Option X5 is used, the Completion of any *section* of the *works*,
- the achievement of the stated Conditions by their Key Dates (Clause 11.2(9) and
- dates on the Accepted Programme for the *Employer* or Others to start work (Clause 25.1).

In effect, the *Contractor* is free to decide when he should correct Defects to avoid delaying these dates (refer to Figure 3).

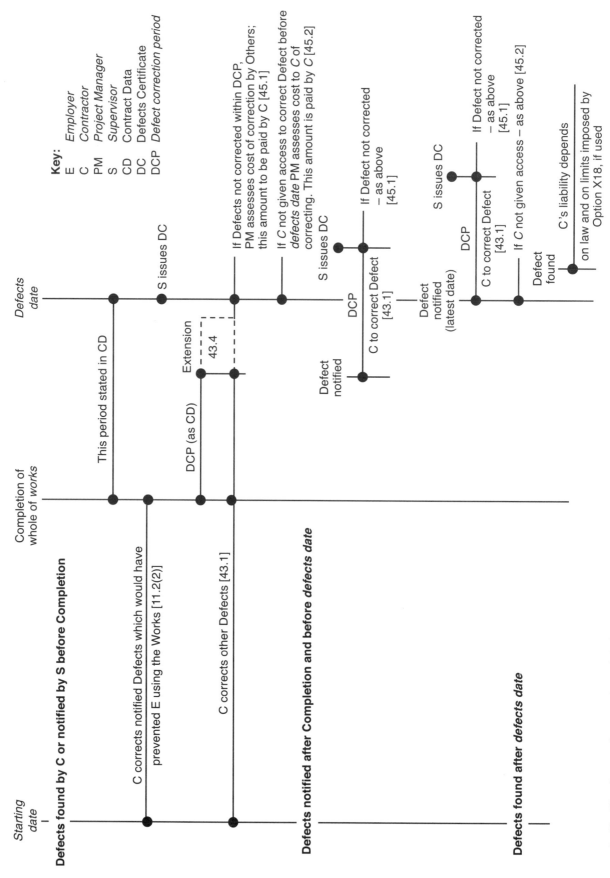

Figure 3. Notification and correction of defects.

43.2 After Completion, the *Contractor* is required to correct any remaining notified Defects, which would not have delayed Completion, before the end of the *defect correction period*. The *defect correction periods*, stated in part one of the Contract Data, only affect the timing of correcting Defects after Completion. Provision is made in the Contract Data format for different lengths of *defect correction period* appropriate for different types of Defect. The length of the *defect correction period* for each type of Defect to be given in the Contract Data depends on

- the kind of Defects likely to be outstanding after Completion and the time needed for their correction,
- the urgency of the *Employer*'s need for their correction, and
- the ease with which access can be given to correct them.

An example of a high degree of urgency for a Defect to be corrected would be one found after Completion which prevents the *Employer* from using the *works*. The *defect correction period* for such a Defect should be stated in the Contract Data part one to be short. If the *Contractor* is then unable to comply, the *Employer* is allowed to have the Defect corrected by other people and recover the incurred cost from the *Contractor* (see explanatory notes on Clause 45.1).

43.3 At the *defects date*, or the end of the last *defect correction period* if later, the *Supervisor* issues a Defects Certificate. This will be used by the *Project Manager* in assessing the final amount due to the *Contractor* (Clause 50.1). The certificate is defined in Clause 11.2(6). The purpose of the last sentence is to preserve the liability of the *Contractor* for undiscovered Defects.

43.4 The procedure in this Clause allows the *Contractor* access to complete outstanding work and correct other Defects after the *Employer* has taken over. Normally, this work can only be done at the *Employer*'s convenience as, after Completion, the *Employer* is obliged to take over the *works*. The clause also states that the *defect correction period* does not start until access and use have been provided.

Accepting Defects **44**

44.1 Although a Defect may be minor, its correction may be costly to the *Contractor* and may delay Completion by a considerable time. Its correction may also cause inconvenience to the *Employer* out of all proportion to the benefits gained. This clause gives a procedure within the contract for accepting a Defect in these circumstances. Either the *Contractor* or the *Project Manager* may propose a change to the Works Information solely to avoid the need to correct a Defect. The other is not obliged to accept the proposal.

44.2 The *Contractor*'s quotation for the proposed change will show a reduction in either time or price or both. In some cases the reduction may be nominal. For example, a nominal price reduction may be acceptable if the effect of the change to the Works Information is not detrimental and if the alternative of correcting the Defect will reduce the likelihood of prompt Completion.

If the quotation is not acceptable, no further action is necessary. If the quotation is accepted by the *Project Manager*, the Works Information, the Prices and the Completion Date are changed accordingly. Such a change to the Works Information is not a compensation event (Clause 60.1(1)).

In terms of liability, the consequences are the same as for other changes to the Works Information. In other words, when the *Project Manager* accepts a Defect and the reduced Prices and earlier Completion Date are agreed, the *Contractor* cannot continue to be held liable for the specific Defect, as if the Defect had still to be corrected under Clause 43.1.

Uncorrected Defects **45**

45.1 This clause states the procedure if the *Contractor* fails to correct a Defect having been given the necessary access. The assessment of the cost of having a Defect corrected by other people does not trigger an assessment under Clause 50.1. This means that most of such amounts accumulate until the *defects date* unless there has been Completion of a *section* of the *works* and a *defect correction period* ends before Completion of the whole of the *works*. When the *Project Manager* is carrying out the assessment following the issue of the Defects Certificate, he will offset the cost of these uncorrected Defects against the release of the second half of the retention money if Option X16 is included. This emphasises the need to make the retention sufficient to cover the likely cost of uncorrected Defects at the *defects date*. This is one of the reasons for the retention arrangement. Quite a high percentage retention should be set in these circumstances because its main purpose is to cover the cost of dealing with uncorrected Defects after Completion. The *retention free amount* should be set as a significant proportion of the contract price so that the retention does not start to accumulate until towards the end of the contract period. It should then produce a significant fund which remains in the *Employer*'s hands until the *defects date* when the extent of the cost of uncorrected Defects is known.

45.2 This clause states the procedure if the Defect has not been corrected due to the lack of access. The criteria the Project Manager uses to assess the amount to be paid is an assessment of the *Contractor*'s cost for carrying out the correction. This may be lower than that assessed in Clause 45.1. It will rarely, if ever, be higher, given that the *Contractor* could also employ Others to correct the Defect in 45.1.

Main Option clauses

Options C, D and E

Tests and Inspections **40**

40.7 See explanatory notes on Clause 40.6.

5 PAYMENT

Payment mechanisms for the main options

The different payment mechanisms for the six main Options are based on the use of three key defined terms

- the Prices (plus, in Option D, an additional term 'Total of the Prices'),
- the Price for Work Done to Date (PWDD), and
- Defined Cost.

Each term is defined for each main Option in Clause 11.2 as summarised briefly in the following table. Abbreviations used in the table are

AS Activity Schedule
BQ Bill of Quantities
DC Defined Cost

Option	The Prices	The Price for Work Done to Date	Defined Cost
A	AS prices for activities 11.2(30)	Total of the Prices for completed activities 11.2(27)	11.2(22)
B	BQ rates and lump sums 11.2(31)	Quantities of completed work at BQ rates and proportions of lump sums 11.2(28)	11.2(22)
C	AS prices for activities 11.2(30)	DC forecast to be paid before next assessment date + Fee 11.2(29)	11.2(23)
D	BQ rates and lump sums 11.2(31) Total of the Prices = BQ rates and lump sums for completed work 11.2(33)	DC forecast to be paid before next assessment date + Fee 11.2(29)	11.2(23)
E	DC + Fee 11.2(32)	DC forecast to be paid before next assessment date + Fee 11.2(29)	11.2(23)
F	DC + Fee 11.2(32)	DC forecast to be paid before next assessment date + Fee 11.2(29)	11.2(24)

These terms are defined in the main Option clauses (see further explanatory notes below). When used in conjunction with the core clauses in Section 5 they establish the payment mechanism for each main Option.

The PWDD is the main component of the amount due to the *Contractor* (see explanatory notes on Clause 50). The use made of the Prices varies between the main Options.

Identified and defined terms	**11**	
Option A	11.2 (27)	The PWDD is the Activity Schedule prices for those activities or groups of activities which have been completed according to the criteria stated in Clause 11.2(27) (see further explanatory notes on Clause 54).
	(30)	The Prices are the basis of the PWDD. In the final assessment the PWDD is the total of the Prices of the completed work. It is important that the *Contractor*, when compiling the *activity schedule*, defines activities and groups of activities, completion of which can be recognised without controversy.
		The effect of a compensation event may be to extend the duration of an activity (or group of activities) so that its completion is delayed. The delay may result in a delay to payment if the activity completion occurs after the assessment date by which the activity was originally expected to have been completed. Where the delay would otherwise cause a seriously adverse effect on the *Contractor*'s cash flow, the *Project Manager* may agree to splitting the activity into two so that payment can be made for the completed work. In deciding whether to agree to this, the *Project Manager* should take account of the extent to which the *Contractor* is collaborating through the early warning procedure and by keeping the Accepted Programme up to date. He should also take account of any delays to the activity or overall programme which are the fault of the *Contractor*.
	(22)	The only use of Defined Cost in Option A is as the basis of the assessment of compensation events. Defined Cost is the cost of the components listed in the Shorter Schedule of Cost Components (see later explanatory notes) for work done by the *Contractor* and his Subcontractors. The cost of preparing quotations for compensation events is specifically excluded (see explanatory notes on Clause 62.1).
Option B	11.2 (28)	The PWDD is calculated using the Bill of Quantities rates and lump sums and the total re-measured quantity of work completed according to the definition and criteria stated in this clause. The 'Bill of Quantities' is defined in Clause 11.2(21), which provides for changes under the contract.
	(31)	The Prices are the basis of the PWDD. In the final account, the PWDD is the total of the Prices of the final quantity of work completed. In this way, the *Contractor* is paid for the actual quantities of work done, not those in the original *bill of quantities*. Option B is therefore a re-measurement contract. It can be used for building contracts where re-measurement is not traditional.
	(22)	The only use of Defined Cost in Option B is as the basis of the assessment of compensation events. Defined Cost is the cost of the components listed in the Shorter Schedule of Cost Components (see later notes) for work done by the *Contractor* and his Subcontractors. The cost of preparing quotations for compensation events is specifically excluded (see explanatory notes on Clause 62.1).
Options C and D	11.2 (29)	The PWDD is the Defined Cost forecast to be paid before the next assessment date plus the Fee as in the cost reimbursable Option E. This is a change in the ECC 3rd edition to improve the *Contractor*'s cash flow.
Option C	11.2 (30)	The Prices in the Activity Schedule (Clause 11.2(20)), are not used to determine the PWDD but the total of the Prices is used as the target in determining (at Completion and in the final assessment) the *Contractor*'s share (see explanatory notes on Clause 53.1 to 53.4). At the times when the *Contractor*'s share is calculated, the Activity Schedule total will have taken account of any compensation events and other changes under the contract and will therefore be a fair target. No re-measurement is involved.
Option D	11.2 (31)	The Prices, using the Bill of Quantities (Clause 11.2(21)), are not used to determine the PWDD.

The target to be used in the calculation of the *Contractor*'s share (at Completion and in the final assessment) needs to take account of not only compensation events and other changes under the contract, but also any re-measurement of work done. In order to ensure a fair target, another defined term 'Total of the Prices' (Clause 11.2(33)) is therefore used in the calculation of the *Contractor*'s share (see explanatory notes on Clauses 53.5 to 53.8). The Prices continue to be the basis of the target and the term is used in other clauses of an Option D contract.

Options C, D and E	11.2 (23)	The basis of the definition of Defined Cost in these Options, before the deduction of Disallowed Cost, has two components

- the amount of payments due to Subcontractors for work which is subcontracted without taking account of certain types of deductions, and
- the cost of components in the Schedule of Cost Components for other work.

The excluded deductions in the first component are listed in the clause in five sub-bullets. The reason for these exclusions is that these amounts are normally deducted from, or not paid to, the *Contractor* by other provisions of the contract. In turn, the *Contractor* may wish to deduct them from his Subcontractors. If they were deducted again when calculating the Defined Cost, they would be deducted twice from the *Contractor*.

Defined Cost is used in calculating the PWDD and in assessing compensation events. It excludes Disallowed Cost as defined separately in Clause 11.2(25) (see below). The cost of preparing quotations for compensation events is allowable as Defined Cost if the people preparing them are in the Working Areas.

The main *Contractor*'s Fee relates to his own overheads, insurance and profit with little risk (e.g. Disallowed Cost) and will be spread over all the work in the contract. Such Fees should be lower than Fees for Options A and B.

	(25)	In the second edition of the ECC, Disallowed Cost included 'a cost which the *Project Manager* decides results from paying a Subcontractor more for a compensation event than is included in the accepted quotation or assessment for the compensation event'. This has been omitted from the third edition. The reason is that it is inequitable to the main *Contractor* in those cases where the subcontract is also under Option C, D or E as the main *Contractor* must pay the cost incurred plus the Fee, which could be more (or less) than the quotation.

In the fifth main bullet of this clause the words 'requirement for' are now changed to 'constraint on' to link this particular Disallowed Cost directly to the definition of Works Information in Clause 11.2(19).

The correction of Defects before Completion is only intended to be a Disallowed Cost if the Defect is caused by the *Contractor* not complying with a constraint on how he is to do the work, for example a prescribed method of working or a constraint on timing of work.

In the sixth main bullet of this clause a rider has been added because some *Project Managers* have been disallowing the cost of Plant and Materials which the *Contractor* bought in good faith but then became surplus as the result of a compensation event.

Option E	11.2 (29)	The PWDD is Defined Cost forecast to be paid before the next assessment date plus the Fee. This is a change in the ECC third edition to improve the *Contractor*'s cash flow.
	(32)	The PWDD becomes the total of the Prices in the final assessment.
Option F	11.2 (29)	The PWDD is Defined Cost forecast to be paid before the next assessment date plus the Fee. This is a change in the ECC edition to improve the *Contractor*'s cash flow.
	(32)	The PWDD becomes the total of the Prices in the final assessment.

(24)   Defined Cost comprises the payments due to Subcontractors and suppliers and the *prices* quoted in the Contract Data for work done by the *Contractor*. It is used to calculate the PWDD and in assessing compensation events. It excludes Disallowed Cost as defined separately in Clause 11.2(26). (See also guidance notes on Option F under 'Contract strategy'.)

Core clauses

Assessing the amount due   **50**

50.1   This clause defines 'assessment dates', from which the dates of both certification and payment are calculated. The first assessment date is determined by the *Project Manager*, preferably after discussion with the *Contractor*, with a view to satisfying the internal procedures of both the *Employer* and the *Contractor*. Thereafter, assessment dates occur after each *assessment interval* until four weeks after the *Supervisor* issues the Defects Certificate.

An additional assessment occurs at Completion of the whole of the *works*.

Subject to a final decision of the *Adjudicator* or *tribunal*, the final assessment date will be four weeks after the date when the *Supervisor* issues the Defects Certificate (the period of four weeks allows time for the *Project Manager* to assess the cost of correcting Defects listed on the Defects Certificate (Clause 45)).

50.2   The core of the amount due to the *Contractor* is the PWDD. All other payments except advanced payments (e.g. for Plant and Materials outside the Working Areas, retention, repayments of advanced payment, damages and tax) are added to or deducted from the PWDD to calculate the amount due. The content of PWDD varies according to which main Option is used (see earlier explanatory notes on payment mechanisms).

Under the UK VAT regulations, payment of VAT by the *Employer* to the *Contractor* is made in response to a VAT invoice provided by the *Contractor*. The *Project Manager* and the *Contractor* should therefore make arrangements to ensure that

- the correct levels of VAT are included in the amount due, and
- the *Contractor*'s VAT invoice is provided for attachment to the *Project Manager*'s certificate.

If the *Employer* does not include within his payment to the *Contractor* the correct amount of sales tax or VAT, the *Contractor* should inform the *Employer* of the error, with a copy to the *Project Manager*. The amount of sales tax or VAT unpaid becomes a debt of the *Employer*.

If the *Employer* uses a self billing system, a *Contractor*'s invoice is not needed and the *Employer*'s remittance document becomes the VAT invoice.

50.3   This clause is designed to provide a powerful motivation on the *Contractor* to submit a programme which contains the information required by the contract. The clause imposes a test to determine whether a quarter of the PWDD should be retained.

If a programme was required to be submitted with the tender, the programme is identified in the Contract Data at the Contract Date. In this situation an Accepted Programme already exists and no amount can be retained under this clause.

If a programme is not identified in the Contract Data it is of vital importance to the management of a contract that a programme complying with Clause 31 is submitted within the period stated in the Contract Data. If a programme is not submitted, the stated retention amount can be withheld.

The test for withholding this retention is one of submission of a programme by the *Contractor*, not acceptance by the *Project Manager*. This avoids retention being imposed as a result of a delay by the *Project Manager* in deciding whether or not to accept the programme.

Clause 50.3 does not apply to any subsequent revision of an Accepted Programme. A different incentive exists on the *Contractor* to keep the Accepted Programme up to date (see Clause 64.2).

50.4 Although assessments of the amount due are the responsibility of the *Project Manager* (Clause 50.1), he takes account of any submissions by the *Contractor* and provides details of his assessment. However the onus remains on the *Project Manager* to assess the amount due even if he has not received a submission from the *Contractor*.

Payment 51
51.1 The latest dates by which the *Project Manager* certifies payments are fixed throughout a contract as each is related to an assessment date. In the majority of cases, certification will be of payment to the *Contractor*.

51.2 The *Employer* can ask for the *Contractor*'s invoice, but the latest dates by which payments are due to be made are also fixed throughout a contract as each is related to an assessment date. Interest is due to the receiving party, either *Employer* or *Contractor*, if a certified payment is not made within the stated period after the assessment date or if a payment is late because the *Project Manager* has not certified it as he should. The *Project Manager* should

- certify payment as early as possible within the week after the assessment date, and
- before the Contract Date, check that the *Employer* is able to pay within the stated period after the assessment date.

The principle that interest is due from the latest date that payment should have been made is applied throughout the contract.

51.3 The same principles on interest due apply to later corrections to certified amounts (including any due to compensation events) made by the *Project Manager* or decided by the *Adjudicator* or the *tribunal*. The last sentence of this clause refers to interest being calculated from the date when the increased amount would have been certified if there had been no dispute or mistake.

51.4 The *interest rate* stated in part one of the Contract Data should be a reliable annual base rate applicable to the territory in which the work is to be done plus a percentage to represent the current commercial rates. Currently in the United Kingdom, the additional percentage should be substantial in order to comply with the Late Payment of Commercial Debts (Interest) Act 1998. Simple interest at the *interest rate* applies for periods less than one year.

Defined Cost 52
52.1 See earlier explanatory notes on the definitions of Defined Cost for Options A and B (11.2(22)), C, D and E (11.2(23)) and Option F (11.2(24)) See also explanatory notes on the Schedule of Cost Components regarding other costs treated as included in the Fee.

Main Option clauses

Option A

The Activity Schedule 54

The Activity Schedule is defined in Clause 11.2(20). A contract which uses Option A is a lump sum contract with the *activity schedule* showing a breakdown of the total lump sum at the Contract Date.

The total of the Prices of the items in the *activity schedule* is the *Contractor*'s offer for Providing the Works. The cost of any items the *Contractor* may have omitted is deemed to be included in the Prices for the other items. There is provision in the conditions for adjusting the Activity Schedule for compensation events and for changes in a planned method of working (see Clauses 63.12 and 54.2). The only other way of changing the Activity Schedule is if the *Project Manager* accepts a quotation for acceleration (Clause 36.3).

The Activity Schedule should include activities such as design tasks and providing Equipment, including temporary works.

There is no automatic provision for payment for Plant and Materials within the Working Areas before they are incorporated into the *works*, i.e. equivalent to 'materials on site'. The *Contractor* may wish to receive earlier payment to improve his cash flow. The required effect can be obtained under Option A by including appropriate items in the Activity Schedule. The special circumstances under which payment might be made for Equipment or Plant and Materials which are outside the Working Areas are covered in Section 7.

If no grouping of activities is included, the *Contractor* is paid for each activity when it is completed (see Clause 11.2(27)).

Milestone payments using Option A

If a group of activities is defined in the *activity schedule*, the *Contractor* is paid for the activities included in it when the whole group is completed. This is how the ECC provides for milestone or stage payments. At each payment assessment date the state of completion of each group of activities is assessed. Only the prices of completed groups are included in the amount due (see further explanatory notes on Clause 50).

The groups of activities should correspond with easily identified stages of the work, e.g. for a building: site preparation, excavation, piling, foundations, structural frame (by floors), floors, cladding, partitions, roof, finishes.

If stage payments are intended for a manufacturer's design, manufacture and installation of a large item of Plant, the instructions to tenderers could state that the *activity schedule* should include the groups of activities necessary to complete stages such as

- confirm acceptance of order by manufacturer,
- acceptance of design,
- stages in the shop assembly of components,
- delivery to Site,
- provision of vendor data, and
- acceptance of performance tests by the *Supervisor.*

54.1 This clause emphasises that the Activity Schedule is only a payment document. It cannot be used to determine what the *Contractor* is to design or build; only to determine payments to the *Contractor* for what he designs or builds.

54.2 An Activity Schedule which contains items that do not represent the *Contractor*'s proposed activities and methods of working will create difficulties in determining payments due. Thus it is important that the Activity Schedule should relate directly to the programme and always be compatible with it (see explanatory notes on Clause 31.4).

54.3   This clause states the criteria by which changes to the Activity Schedule are to be judged. For instance, the changed Prices are not reasonably distributed between the activities on the revised Activity Schedule and are instead loaded against certain activities. The total of the Prices must not be changed except as a result of a compensation event or an acceleration. The criteria do not attempt to restrict changes to cash flow resulting from revisions to the Activity Schedule.

Option B

The Bill of Quantities   **55**

55.1   This clause emphasises that the Bill of Quantities is only a payment document. It cannot be used to determine what the *Contractor* is to design or build; but only to determine payment to the *Contractor* for what he designs or builds.

Options C and D

Assessing the amount due   **50**

50.6   The *Contractor* is reimbursed by the *Employer* in the same currency as the payments made by him. Nevertheless, the Fee and the *Contractor*'s share are paid in the *currency of the contract*. Calculations use the *exchange rates* identified in the optional statement for Options C, D, E or F in part one of the Contract Data.

Defined Cost   **52**

52.2   This clause lists the accounts and records which the *Contractor* is required to keep and which are essential for calculating the Defined Cost. If any further records are required, details should be given in the Works Information.

The *Contractor*'s share   **53**
Option C 53.1 and 53.2
Option D 53.5 and 53.6

The purpose of the *Contractor*'s share is to encourage effective management control of the final PWDD (total Defined Cost (Clause 11.2 (23)) plus the Fee) relative to the target (in Option C, the total of the Prices (Clause 11.2(30)) and in Option D the Total of the Prices (see explanatory notes on Clause 11.2(33)). The *Contractor* receives a share of any saving or pays a share of excess when the final PWDD is compared to the target (adjusted for compensation events under Clause 63 and for Option D, also for re-measurement).

The *Employer* will normally wish to vary the size of the *Contractor*'s share depending on the extent of the saving below or the excess above the target. The mechanism for calculating the *Contractor*'s share is provided by the *Employer* in his preparation of the tender documents by completing the format in part one of the Contract Data.

Each *range* is defined by levels of the ratio PWDD/Prices expressed as a percentage. The *Employer* decides the *Contractor*'s *share percentage* for each *range* to give the appropriate motivation to suit the objectives of the contract.

For example, in an Option C contract, assume that the Contract Data states that

• The *Contractor's share percentages* and the *share ranges* are

Share range	Contractor's share percentage
less than 80%	15%
from 80% to 90%	30%
from 90% to 110%	50%
greater than 110%	20%

If at Completion of the whole of the *works*, the total of the Prices (having been adjusted for compensation events) is £100K, the Contract Data table becomes in effect

Final PWDD	Contractor's share percentage
less than 80K	15%
from 80K to 90K	30%
from 90K to 110K	50%
greater than 110K	20%

Examples of possible outcomes are

a) Final PWDD = £75K
Saving under total of the Prices = £25K
Comprising three increments:

80K	= 5K @ 15% = 0.75K
80K to 90K	= 10K @ 30% = 3.00K
90K to 110K	= 10K @ 50% = 5.00K
Contractor's share	= £8.75K
(paid **by** *Employer*)	

b) Final PWDD = £95K
Saving under total of the Prices = £5K
Comprising one increment:

90K to 110K	= 5K @ 50% = 2.5K
Contractor's share	= £2.5K
(paid **by** *Employer*)	

c) Final PWDD = £115K
Excess over total of the Prices = £15K
Comprising two increments:

90K to 110K	= 10K @ 50% = 5.0K
Greater than 110K	= 5K @ 20% = 1.0K
Contractor's share	= £6.0K
(paid **to** *Employer*)	

The above example also applies to an Option D contract if 'total of the Prices' is replaced by 'Total of the Prices'

The other potential source of profit for the *Contractor* is the Fee. The *Contractor's share percentages* should be determined in a particular contract to provide the appropriate level of incentive to the *Contractor* to minimise the final PWDD. The extent of financial risk to the Parties in the event of the final PWDD exceeding the total of the Prices can be varied between two extremes

• a guaranteed maximum price (excluding the effects of Compensation Events) to the *Employer* can be achieved by stating the *Contractor's share percentage* to be 100% above that price,
• a minimum Fee to the *Contractor* can be encouraged by stating the *Contractor's share percentage* is to be 0% above a stated price.

Option C 53.3 and 53.4
Option D 53.7 and 53.8

Payment of the target share is made in two stages. Firstly, in the payment due following Completion of the whole of the *works*, and secondly, in the final payment made after the issue of the Defects Certificate. In calculating the final *Contractor*'s share, the *Project Manager* should take account of costs incurred which the *Contractor* has not been able to pay (for example because an invoice has not been submitted).

Interim payments of the *Contractor*'s share are not provided. The Prices tendered by a *Contractor* have the main purpose of establishing the target. It is not intended that their build-up should provide a realistic forecast of cash flow and they are unlikely to be comparable with the PWDD at any interim stage. Any delays in assessing compensation events would further distort the calculation.

This danger of serious under or over payment of an interim *Contractor*'s share before Completion has led to the policy of an estimated payment at Completion which is corrected in the assessment of the final amount due.

Option C

The Activity Schedule 54

54.1 This clause emphasises the fact that the Activity Schedule is only a payment document. It cannot be used to determine what the *Contractor* is to design or build; only to determine the *Contractor*'s share.

54.2 It is important that the Activity Schedule should relate directly to the programme and always be compatible with it (see explanatory notes on Clause 31.4).

54.3 This clause states the criteria by which changes to the Activity Schedule are to be judged. For instance, the changed Prices are not reasonably distributed between the activities on the revised Activity Schedule and are instead loaded against certain activities. The total of the Prices must not be changed except as a result of a compensation event or an acceleration.

Option D

The Bill of Quantities 55

55.1 This clause emphasises that the Bill of Quantities is only a payment document. It cannot be used to determine what the *Contractor* is to design or build; only to determine the *Contractor*'s share.

Options E and F

Assessing the amount due 50

50.7 The *Contractor* is reimbursed by the *Employer* in the same currency as the payments made by him. Nevertheless, the Fee is paid in the *currency of the contract*. Calculations use the *exchange rates* identified in the optional statement for options C, D, E or F in part one of the Contract Data.

Defined Cost 52

52.2 This clause lists the accounts and records which the *Contractor* is required to keep and which are essential for calculating the Defined Cost. If any further records are required, details should be given in the Works Information.

6 COMPENSATION EVENTS

Introduction

This section consists of six main clauses.

- Clause 60 defines compensation events.
- Clause 61 deals with notification, by either the *Project Manager* or the *Contractor*, that a compensation event has occurred.
- Clause 62 covers the submission of quotations for compensation events.
- Clause 63 sets out the rules for assessing the effects of a compensation event (time and money).
- Clause 64 covers assessments made by the *Project Manager*.
- Clause 65 explains how any changed prices or dates are incorporated into the contract.

Core clauses

Compensation events   60

Compensation events are events which, if they occur, and do not arise from the *Contractor*'s fault, entitle the *Contractor* to be compensated for any effect the event has on the Prices and the Completion Date or a Key Date. The assessment of a compensation event is always of its effect on the Prices, the Completion Date, and any Key Date affected by the event. Any event may entitle the *Contractor* to additional payment and also to additional time. In the case of some events, the results may be reduced payment to the *Contractor*. (Further notes on the principles of compensation events are included in the introduction to these guidance notes.)

Compensation events are listed in the core clauses, the Options and the Contract Data. The main list is in the core Clause 60.1, which includes compensation events (1) to (19). Events applicable to main Options B and D are stated in Clauses 60.4, 60.5 and 60.6. Other compensation events are stated in secondary Option Clauses X2.1, X14.2, X15.2 and Y(UK)2.4.

Option Z may be used by the *Employer* to insert additional compensation events. If he does so, the effect is to take the risk of costs and delay arising from the event from the *Contractor*. The event must be described precisely.

Clause 60.1 does not include an industrial dispute as a compensation event unless it is a dispute classed as an *Employer*'s risk by Clause 80.1. In such a case it becomes a compensation event through Clause 60.1(14). Employers vary as to the policy they wish to adopt towards the risk of industrial disputes. Outside the United Kingdom the legal, cultural or religious climate can also affect policy.

The following are examples of possible additional compensation events for specific contracts. None are applicable generally.

- The cycle time for tunnel excavation exceeds eight working hours for more than four consecutive cycles for reasons outside the control of the *Contractor*.
- The water level in the estuary at Point A rises to more than 26.00 metres above ordnance datum.
- The minimum wage ordered by the Government of X exceeds £Y per hour.
- The amount of water flowing into the main tunnel exceeds 5000 litres per hour before concreting of the invert is completed.
- Work is stopped to allow a ship to pass on more than 24 occasions in a given period.

Changing the Works Information	60.1 (1)	Variations to the *works* are made by a *Project Manager*'s instruction to change the Works Information. The authority given to the *Project Manager* for this purpose is in Clause 14.3. A variation may comprise deletion or addition of work or alteration to work. It may include changes to the *Employer*'s design, to design criteria or to performance requirements for the *Contractor*'s design. Issue of a revised drawing or specification is a compensation event. Clarifications of previously issued drawings or specifications are only made by changing the Works Information. Consequently, all such clarifications are compensation events although not all of them will lead to additional time or monies (see Clause 61.4). There may be many reasons for changing the Works Information. They include changes made in order to eliminate an illegality or impossibility (Clause 18) or to resolve an ambiguity or inconsistency (Clause 17).

The clause states two exceptions to a change to the Works Information being a compensation event.

- The procedure for accepting a Defect is stated in Clause 44. An instruction to change the Works Information after acceptance of the *Contractor*'s quotation under Clause 44.2 is not a compensation event.
- A change to the *Contractor*'s design made at his own request is not a compensation event. The clause also gives precedence to the Works Information in part one of the Contract Data over the Works Information in part two of the Contract Data. Thus the *Contractor* should ensure that the Works Information he prepares and submits with his tender as part two of the Contract Data complies with the requirements of the Works Information in part one of the Contract Data. (See also explanatory notes on Clause 21.2.)

Access to and use of the Site	(2)	The *Employer*'s obligations to give the *Contractor* access to and use of a part of the Site are stated in Clause 33.
Provision by the *Employer*	(3)	The Works Information should give details of anything, such as Plant and Materials, which the *Employer* is to provide and of any restrictions on when it is to be provided. The *Contractor* is required to include this information on the programme under Clause 31.2.
Stopping work or changing a Key Date	(4)	Clause 34.1 gives the *Project Manager* the authority to instruct the *Contractor* to stop or not to start work. There are several reasons why the *Project Manager* may give such an instruction, e.g. for reasons of safety. He may also vary a Key Date (Clause 14.3), for example to suit actual progress on other works related to the contract.
Work of the *Employer* or Others	(5)	The Works Information should give details of the order and timing of work to be done by the *Employer* or Others. The *Contractor* is required to include this information on the programme under Clause 31.2.
Reply to a communication	(6)	Various periods are given in particular clauses for reply by the *Project Manager* and *Supervisor* and a general *period for reply* is given in the Contract Data. The obligation to reply within the relevant period is stated in Clause 13.3.
Objects of value	(7)	The procedure for dealing with objects of value or of historical or other interest found within the Site is stated in Clause 73.1.
Changing a decision	(8)	The *Project Manager* and *Supervisor* are able to change decisions made under the authority given to them in the contract, in the same way as they made their original decisions.
Withholding an acceptance	(9)	Various clauses state reasons why the *Project Manager* is entitled not to accept a submission or proposal from the *Contractor*. If he withholds acceptance for any other reason, as he is entitled to do under Clause 13.8, it is a compensation event.

Searching	(10)	The *Supervisor* can instruct the *Contractor* to search for a Defect under Clause 42.1. Usually searches are instigated where faulty design, construction or manufacture is suspected.
Delayed tests and inspections	(11)	The testing and inspection work to be carried out by the *Supervisor* is stated in the Works Information. Under Clause 40.5, the *Supervisor* is required to do this work without causing unnecessary delay.

Wherever possible the Works Information should include estimates of the time that the Supervisor needs for any of his tests. This will avoid arguments about what constitutes 'unnecessary delays'.

Physical conditions	60.1 (12)

For many years, it has been the practice in construction contracts for the *Employer* to take the risk of physical conditions which have been described in such terms as 'those which could not reasonably have been foreseen by an experienced contractor'. The interpretation of such clauses has been the source of many disputes, mainly because a difficult judgement is involved. The ECC includes an overhauled but not radically different procedure.

This compensation event is limited to those physical conditions which are encountered within the Site and not any other parts of the Working Areas. Since most claims for unforeseen conditions are in respect of ground conditions, the more information concerning ground conditions which is made available to tenderers by the *Employer*, the greater the certainty with which appropriate allowances can be made in tendering. It is important that the ground information provided is both correct and relevant to the risks faced. It may be advisable also to prepare and provide interpretation of factual data, provided this is prepared by a specialist. In this way tenderers are able to tender on a common basis.

One method of reducing disputes on this topic is to define in the contract the boundary line between the risks carried by the *Employer* and *Contractor*, i.e. to state what tenderers should allow for in their tenders. This can be done, for example, in tunnel works or extensive foundation works by stating the boundary conditions. This should be done by using Option Z to state boundary conditions covering such matters as

* soil characteristics,
* levels of rock/soil interface,
* groundwater levels,
* permeability limits, and
* overbreak in rock excavation.

Tenderers will then be able to tender on a common basis, knowing that they must allow in their pricing for the occurrence of physical conditions within the stated boundary conditions.

The last paragraph of Clause 60.1(12) clarifies the position about the basis of an assessment of any valid 'physical conditions' compensation event.

Note that under some circumstances an event which arises as a result of unforeseen ground conditions could qualify as a 'Clause 19 event', in which case the *Project Manager* assumes responsibility for managing the consequences.

Adverse weather	Rather than rely on the subjective generalisations about 'exceptionally
60.1 (13)	

Adverse weather 60.1 (13)

Rather than rely on the subjective generalisations about 'exceptionally inclement weather' sometimes included in standard forms of contract, the ECC includes a more objective and measurable approach. The purpose is to make available for each contract *weather data*, referred to in the Contract Data, normally compiled by an independent authority, establishing the levels of selected relevant weather conditions for the Site for each calendar month which have had a period of return of more than ten years. If weather conditions more adverse than these levels occur it is a compensation event. Weather which the *weather data* show is likely to occur within a ten year period is the *Contractor*'s risk in relation to both cost and time.

The time of occurrence of all compensation events is when the action or lack of action describing the event in Clause 60.1 takes place. In the case of weather it is the day when the stated test shows that weather conditions are recorded as having occurred within a calendar month which 'do not occur on average less frequently than once in ten years'. The test is the comparison of the *weather measurements* with the *weather data*. The compensation event can then be notified under Clause 61.3 and its effect can be assessed at the end of the month when the extent of the weather exceeding the ten year return *weather data* is known. The process starts again at the beginning of each month.

If the *weather measurements* are recorded at an independent weather station and not on Site, the figures will not normally be available until a few days after the end of each month.

This compensation event is concerned with weather occurring only at the place stated in the Contract Data. If weather occurring at some distance from the Site could produce some risk, such as flooding on the Site, the allocation of risk should be dealt with by special compensation events, such as the second example in the introductory notes on Clause 60 (page 68).

Weather characteristics for extended construction sites, such as cross country pipelines, may vary considerably along the length of the Site. In such cases the Site can be divided into areas, each chosen to have reasonably uniform weather characteristics throughout the area. Appropriate *weather measurements* and *weather data* can then be used for each area, with the Contract Data suitably amended.

The provisions for weather in the ECC were developed in consultation with the United Kingdom's Meteorological Office (the Met Office) which can provide advice and information about the availability of recorded weather data. There is a charge for providing data. The contract makes no recommendations about who should pay; it is suggested that the *Employer* should obtain the *weather data* and the *Contractor* obtain the *weather measurements*.

In most of the more populous parts of the United Kingdom, there is sufficient coverage of Met Office weather stations to be able to relate to any particular site. The Met Office is also able to advise on methods of recording the actual *weather measurements*. In many cases, measurements taken at a neighbouring weather station will be sufficiently representative of the weather on the Site, and there are obvious advantages in having *weather data* and *weather measurements* recorded at the same place.

The Met Office can also advise on expected weather conditions on sites outside the United Kingdom and, if necessary, recommend a meteorological authority to provide the *weather data*. Many countries have authorities similar to the Met Office where similar data is available. In other countries there may be little established data but it may still be possible, with the advice of the appropriate weather authority, to agree limiting values approximating to the 'once in ten years' average. This would provide an adequate basis for an adverse weather compensation event. Where no recorded data are available, the assumed *weather data* are entered in the Contract Data.

In some countries the criteria in this Clause may not be appropriate to achieve a reasonable balance of weather risk between the Parties. For example, a violent but short lived storm may devastate a site for weeks, but not exceed the once in ten years return period for the particular month. An amendment to this Clause should be considered in such cases, possibly using Clause 60.1(19).

Weather parameters

The choice of weather measurements depends upon the types of construction operation to be carried out and the weather characteristics of the area.

Clause 60.1(13) refers to the *weather measurements*. Part one of the Contract Data includes four measurements for which ten year 'return period statistics' for each calendar month may be required. Met Office data are recorded by calendar month. These measurements have been selected as being the minimum weather aspects which can have a significant effect on construction work in the United Kingdom and countries with similar climates. They are

- the cumulative rainfall (mm) (this includes the equivalent rainfall corresponding to falls of snow),
- the number of days with rainfall more than 5 mm (a measure of the days when outside work may be interrupted by rain),
- the number of days with minimum air temperature less than 0 degrees Celsius, and
- the number of days with snow lying at a stated time GMT (in the United Kingdom, Met Office readings are taken at 09:00 hours GMT; the time may vary in other countries).

Space is left in the Contract Data part one for adding other measurements pertinent to the Site in question or the operations to be carried out. For instance, if tower cranes are to be used, a reference to the number of working hours or days in a month in which the wind speed exceeds a critical level may be appropriate. The actual wind speed at the Site would need to be related to the speed at the reference weather station. The Met Office or local weather authority should be consulted about the practicality of additional measurements.

The final sentence of the Clause makes it clear that only the 'extra' adverse weather is to be taken into account in assessing the effects of the compensation event. For example, if the number of days with rainfall more than 5 mm in February is stated in the *weather data* to be 6, and the weather measurements record a total of 8, any delay is assessed on the basis of the 2 'extra' days.

Weather records during the contract

The data routinely recorded at a weather station close to the Site could be used as an alternative to recording on the Site. If there is not a weather station nearby, the *weather measurements* should be made using gauges and equipment installed at the place stated in the Contract Data.

Note that under some circumstances an event which arises as a result of adverse weather could qualify as a 'Clause 19 event', in which case the *Project Manager* assumes responsibility for managing the consequences.

Employer's risk events 60.1 (14)

The *Employer*'s risks are stated in Clause 80.1. Any additional *Employer*'s risks should be stated in part one of the Contract Data.

Note that under some circumstances an event which is an *Employer*'s risk event could qualify as a 'Clause 19 event', in which case the *Project Manager* assumes responsibility for managing the consequences.

Employer's use of the works	60.1 (15)	The *Employer* may use a part of the *works* before Completion and, unless the use is for the reasons stated in Clause 35.2, he takes over the part. If take over occurs before the Completion Date, it is a compensation event. It is therefore important that the Works Information should state the reasons why the *Employer* may require to use parts of the *works* before Completion.

For instance, he may require access across parts of the *works* for his own purposes. Alternatively, the *Contractor* may request the *Employer* to use part of the *works* to suit the *Contractor*'s method of working.

Under Clause 35.2, take over would not occur in either of these circumstances and there would be no compensation event.

Materials, facilities, etc. for tests	60.1 (16)	Under Clause 40.2, the *Employer* is required to provide materials, facilities and samples for tests as stated in the Works Information.
Assumptions about compensation events	60.1 (17)	Under Clause 61.6 (see later notes), the *Project Manager* may state assumptions to be used in the assessment of a compensation event. If he later notifies corrections to such assumptions, the notification is a separate compensation event.

These *Project Manager*'s assumptions should not be confused with any forecast or estimates made by the *Contractor* in his assessment of a compensation event. If the *Contractor*'s forecast is later shown to have been wrong, neither the *Contractor* nor the *Project Manager* can change it (see Clause 65.2).

Employer's breach of contract	60.1 (18)	This is an 'umbrella' clause to include breaches of contract by the *Employer* within the compensation event procedure. Without this Clause, in most jurisdictions the *Contractor*'s only remedy for a breach of contract by the *Employer* would be under the law. However, because of the effects of this clause and Clause 63.4, the *Contractor*'s only remedy is under the contract.
Other events	60.1 (19)	This is a 'force majeure' event. The event must be such that it either stops the *Contractor* from completing the *works* (an absolute test) or stops him from completing by the time shown on the Accepted Programme.

A delay to planned Completion which can (as opposed to will) be recovered by acceleration, by increased resources, or by adjusting the programme does not stop the *Contractor* from completing on time. The *Contractor* must demonstrate that there is no reasonable means by which he can complete the *works* on time for the event to be recognised under the second bullet point.

	60.2, 60.3	The information which the *Contractor* is assumed to have taken account of in 60(12) is listed in Clause 60.2. Clause 60.3 states the 'contra proferentem' rule regarding inconsistencies in the Site Information, for which the *Employer* is responsible.
Notifying compensation events	**61** 61.1	This procedure would normally apply to compensation events 1, 4, 7, 8, 10, 15 and 17 each of which is due to an action by the *Project Manager* or *Supervisor*. When the event occurs, the *Project Manager* notifies the *Contractor* and instructs him to submit quotations. Where the compensation event results from the *Contractor*'s fault or where quotations have already been submitted, quotations are not instructed. However, in order to avoid doubt in such cases, it is advisable that when the *Project Manager* notifies the compensation event, he should give his reason for not instructing quotations. The *Contractor* is required to act on the instruction or changed decision.

It is important that the *Project Manager* notifies such compensation events, without waiting for the *Contractor* to do so. If he does not do so he may leave the *Employer* open to late claims from the *Contractor*, because the time-bar in Clause 61.3 does not apply to these types of events.

61.2 This clause deals with the situation where the *Project Manager* is considering issuing an instruction or changing a decision but first requires to know what effect this would have on cost and time, for example when he is considering a change to the Works Information (Clause 60.1(1)). He has the authority to instruct the *Contractor* to submit quotations as a first step.

61.3 This procedure would normally apply to the compensation events not covered by those in Clause 61.1. These are events which arise from

- a failure by the *Employer*, *Project Manager*, *Supervisor* or Others to fulfil their obligations (compensation events 2, 3, 5, 6, 11, 16 and 18),
- the *Project Manager* withholding an acceptance for a reason not stated in the contract (compensation event 9), or
- a happening not caused by any party (compensation events 12, 13, 14 and 19).

It would also apply to an event which the *Project Manager* should have notified under Clause 61.1, but did not do so. In such cases, the *Contractor* initiates the procedure by notifying the *Project Manager*.

To avoid having to deal with a compensation event long after it has occurred there is a time limit on notification by the *Contractor*. Failure to comply with this time limit 'time-bars' the *Contractor* from any compensation for the event unless the event is one which the *Project Manager* should have notified under Clause 61.1.

61.4 This clause lists the four tests which the *Project Manager* applies to an event notified by the *Contractor* in order to decide whether or not to instruct the *Contractor* to submit quotations for its effect. If the *Project Manager* decides that the event fails any one of the tests he notifies the *Contractor* and no further action is required unless the *Contractor* disputes the decision and refers it to the *Adjudicator*.

In many circumstances, the *Project Manager* will be able to give his decision within a week of the *Contractor*'s notification. With more complicated events, a longer period will be desirable to ensure adequate time for a properly considered decision. Provision is made for such longer periods subject to the *Contractor*'s agreement.

The final paragraph of this clause protects the *Contractor* against a delay by the *Project Manager* in responding to the *Contractor*'s notification.

61.5 The *Project Manager* should include in an instruction to submit quotations his decision on whether or not the *Contractor* gave an early warning which an experienced contractor could have given. This has an effect on the assessment of the event (see Clause 63.4).

61.6 In some cases, the nature of the compensation event may be such that it is impossible to prepare a sufficiently accurate quotation. One example of this is where unexpected physical conditions are encountered (compensation event 12) but their extent is unknown. In these cases, quotations are submitted on the basis of assumptions stated by the *Project Manager* in his instruction to the *Contractor*. If the assumptions later prove to be wrong, the *Project Manager*'s notification of their correction is a separate compensation event (Clause 60.1(17)).

Apart from this situation, the assessment of compensation events cannot be revised (Clause 65.2). Since each quotation can include due allowance for risk (Clause 63.5) and the early warning procedure should minimise the effects of unexpected problems, the need for later review is minimal, and the benefits to both Parties of fixed time and cost effects far outweigh any such need.

Quotations for 62
compensation events 62.1 There may be several ways of adjusting plans for the work to deal with a compensation event and its consequences. The procedure in this clause enables the *Project Manager* to consider different options. For instance, it may be more beneficial to the *Employer* to achieve earlier Completion at a greater cost than an alternative of later Completion at a lower cost. The clause also provides for the *Contractor* to submit quotations using methods other than those assumed in the *Project Manager's* instruction. For instance, the *Contractor* may be able to use a specialised item of Equipment, which the *Project Manager* did not realise was available.

The *Project Manager* is required to discuss possible ways of dealing with the event with the *Contractor* before instructing him to submit quotations. This is intended to avoid wasting the *Contractor's* resources in preparing quotations for methods which are not practicable.

In Options C, D, E and F, the *Contractor's* cost of preparing quotations for compensation events will usually be included in Defined Cost (assuming that quotations are prepared by people working in the Working Areas), as defined for the main Option being used, and thus in the PWDD.

In the priced Options A and B, the cost of preparing quotations for compensation events is specifically excluded from Defined Cost (Clause 11.2(22)). Tenderers should therefore allow in their tendered *fee percentages* for such costs as they are not reimbursed directly.

This policy has been adopted in Options A and B in order to retain the certainty of the Prices relative to the work done. However, some *Employer's* make special arrangements to reimburse costs of preparing quotations in particular circumstances, for example

- when the effect is very large, or
- when the *Employer* is asking for multiple quotations for significant design changes, especially when alternative solutions are being considered.

62.2 Quotations comprise a 'package' of time and money as, in most situations, it is impossible to consider either in isolation. The use of the term 'quotation' is not the same as the normal use in commerce, i.e. the free submission of an offer. Quotations are based on an assessment of forecast or recorded Defined Cost (Clause 63.1) and time (Clause 63.3) arising from the compensation event. A build-up of each quotation is required to be submitted by the *Contractor*. If re-programming of remaining work is affected, the quotation should include a revised programme, showing, amongst other things, any change to planned Completion or a Key Date.

If several minor compensation events occur within a short period, it can be counter-productive to produce a revised programme for each one – particularly as the status of quotations for earlier ones will not yet be finalised. Some project managers have adopted a procedure where all the compensation events notified in one month are considered in one revised programme.

62.3 The time limits are intended to promote efficient management of the contract procedures. The time limits for submission and for the *Project Manager's* reply may, however, be extended under certain conditions, as stated in Clause 62.5. An example of the need for this flexibility is when a weather compensation event (Clause 60.1(13)) occurs very early in a calendar month. The effect of the event cannot be assessed until the end of the month when the extent of the weather exceeding the ten year return *weather data* becomes known. If the event is notified by both the *Contractor* and the *Project Manager* immediately, the time remaining to the end of the month may be more than the three weeks allowed for the *Contractor* to quote. An extension of the time to quote would then be necessary.

The four possible categories of reply by the *Project Manager* are listed. The third category may result from the *Project Manager* deciding not to proceed with a proposed change to the Works Information. This is likely to happen when the cost of the change is too high or the delay too great. The *Project Manager* has absolute discretion in such a case on whether to proceed.

62.4 This procedure permits revision of quotations. In practice, this will usually follow discussion between the *Project Manager* and the *Contractor* on the details of the submitted quotations. When instructing a revised quotation the *Project Manager* may alter or add to the assumptions made under Clause 61.6. Again, time limits for submission of the revised quotation are stated.

62.5 This clause provides for the extension of the time limits stated in Clause 62.3 which may be necessary with the more major or far-reaching events. The *Project Manager* and the *Contractor* must agree to the extension before the expiry of the times stated.

62.6 It is important that the *Project Manager* does not delay the assessment of compensation events, by, for example, waiting until the changed work is complete before deciding whether or not to accept the *Contractor*'s quotation. This clause protects the *Contractor* from such delays by the *Project Manager*. Once the quotation is treated as accepted it is implemented (third bullet of Clause 65.1). The only remedy the *Employer* then has if he does not agree with the quotation is adjudication.

Assessing compensation events 63

63.1 Assessment of compensation events as they affect Prices is based on their effect on Defined Cost plus the Fee. This is different from some standard forms of contract where variations are valued using the rates and prices in the contract as a basis. The reason for this policy is that no compensation event for which a quotation is required is due to the fault of the *Contractor* or relates to a matter which is at his risk under the contract. It is therefore appropriate to reimburse the *Contractor* his forecast additional costs (or actual additional costs if work has already been done) arising from the compensation event. Disputes arising from the applicability of contract rates are avoided.

There is provision in Options B and D, in Clause 63.13, for rates and prices in the Bill of Quantities to be used in the assessment instead of Defined Cost, if the *Project Manager* and the *Contractor* agree.

Ideally, the assessment will be the forecast of Defined Cost of work which is yet to be done, but it may include an element of incurred Defined Cost for work which has been done (e.g. when an emergency instruction has had to be given, or for a weather compensation event).

Where the work to be done is changed, it is important that the assessment is based upon the change in forecast or recorded Defined Cost. The clause gives no authority for the price for the originally specified work to be deleted or for the forecast Defined Cost of all work now required to be used as the basis for a new price.

If the Works Information originally included a piece of work (a) which is now to be replaced by a piece of work (b), the compensation event is assessed as the difference between the forecast Defined Cost of (b) and the forecast Defined Cost of (a). The Fee is then added to this difference and the resulting total amount is used to change the Prices. The original price for (a) does not enter the assessment.

Similarly, if the effect of a compensation event is only to delete future work, the assessment is based on the forecast Defined Cost of that work plus the Fee, not simply a deletion of the price for the deleted work. There is, of course, no obstruction to the *Project Manager* and the *Contractor* agreeing to delete the price if both are satisfied that it adequately represents the reduction in forecast Defined Cost plus the Fee.

If some or all the work arising from a compensation event has already been done, Defined Cost should be readily assessable from records. Forecasting future Defined Cost is less straightforward. Estimates of resources are required and productivity rates for Equipment and labour. For Options C, D and E, pricing of the various components of Defined Cost is normally based on the Schedule of Cost Components (SCC) with the associated percentages tendered in the Contract Data part two, although the Shorter SCC may be used in some circumstances (see Clause 63.15). The Shorter SCC is used with Options A and B. The Fee is calculated in accordance with Clause 11.2(8).

Clause 63.1 now pinpoints the date when there is a switch from recorded costs to forecast costs included in a quotation. This prevents the practice of a *Project Manager* making a retrospective and selective choice between a quotation and the final recorded costs of dealing with a comparison event. This practice was never intended to be allowed because it clearly disadvantages the *Contractor* and, if adopted, will inevitably lead to adversarialism and game playing.

The switch date has been set as the date the *Project Manager* instructs the *Contractor* to submit a quotation rather than the date the quotation is submitted. This supports the intention of the NEC that assessments will usually be forecasts of the cost of work yet to be done. Where work has had to start before the quotation has been submitted or even before the instruction to submit was given it is inevitable that the forecast component of quotation will be influenced by the cost already incurred. Nevertheless, for most cases, the inclusion in the clause of a switch date set early in the assessment process reinforces the point that compensation events are not cost-reimbursable but are assessed on forecasts with the *Contractor* taking some risk.

There is no reference to the first instruction to submit a quotation. This means that if there is an instruction to submit a revised quotation the switch date becomes the date of that later instruction. If work has been done between the two instructions the revised quotation will take account of the cost incurred.

63.2 Only certain compensation events can reduce the Prices. These are listed in the main options as follows:

- Option A: 63.10
- Option B: 60.4, 60.6 and 63.10
- Option C: 63.11
- Option D: 60.4, 60.6 and 63.11
- Options E and F: none

In addition, the Prices can be reduced by the application of Option X2.

All other compensation events listed in Clause 60.1 and in the optional clauses cannot lead to reduced Prices, even if their effect is to reduce Defined Cost plus Fee.

There is provision, however, for additional compensation events to be included in the Contract Data. Such an additional compensation event can only lead to increased or unchanged Prices unless an additional condition, using Option Z, states specifically that it can also lead to reduced Prices.

63.3 No compensation event can result in a reduction in the time for carrying out the *works*, i.e. an earlier Completion Date or Key Date. Only an acceleration as agreed under Clause 36 can result in an earlier Completion Date or Key Date.

The first stage in assessing whether the Completion Date or a Key Date should be delayed as a result of a compensation event is to adjust the Accepted Programme to take account of the compensation event with any appropriate adjustments to time risk allowances (Clause 63.6). Any float in the programme before planned Completion is available to mitigate or avoid any consequential delay to planned Completion. However any terminal float between planned Completion and the Completion Date and the planned achievement of the Condition required by a Key Date and that Key Date is not available (see explanatory notes on Clause 31.2). If planned Completion is delayed, the Completion Date is delayed by the same period. If planned Completion is not delayed, the Completion Date is unchanged. If the adjusted programme shows that achievement of the Key Date will be delayed, the Key Date is delayed by the same period.

63.4   If any of the compensation events occurs the Parties' sole remedy is to use the compensation event procedure. Therefore if the *Employer* breaches the contract the *Contractor* must use this route (see Clause 60.1(18)), rather than pursuing damages. This prevents the *Contractor* trying to circumvent the time limits in the contract.

63.5   The *Contractor*'s duty to give an early warning is stated in Clause 16.1. The sanction if the *Contractor* fails to give early warning is stated in this clause. It is possible that early warning could have allowed actions to be taken which would have reduced costs and saved time. It is important that the *Project Manager* notifies the *Contractor* of his decision that early warning should have been given (Clause 61.5) so that the *Contractor* knows the correct basis for his assessment and the nature of the early warning.

63.6   Allowances for risk must be included in forecasts of Defined Cost and Completion in the same way that the *Contractor* allows for risks when pricing his tender. The value of the allowance is greater when the work is uncertain and there is a high chance of a *Contractor*'s risk happening. It is least when the uncertainties are small and when the work is to be done by resources already on Site whose output rates can be predicted relatively accurately.

If there is considerable uncertainty over the effects of a compensation event the *Project Manager* can decide, in consultation with *Contractor* where appropriate, to limit this uncertainty by stating the assumptions the *Contractor* is to base his quotation on (Clause 61.6). In effect he is limiting the *Contractor*'s risk, but not necessarily removing it. Risk allowances for cost and time are still permitted in the assessment.

63.7   This clause protects the *Employer* against inefficiency on the part of the *Contractor*. The reference to changing the Accepted Programme is made so that it is clear that the *Contractor* is expected to alter his arrangements when necessary.

63.8   This clause expresses the 'contra proferentem' rule, which interprets a clause containing an ambiguity or inconsistency against the party responsible for drafting the document in which it occurs.

The *Project Manager*'s assessments   **64**

64.1   The four circumstances in which the *Project Manager* assesses a compensation event are stated. They are all derived from some failure of the *Contractor*. The second results from the *Contractor* not assessing the compensation event correctly in accordance with the contract. This means that the changes to the Prices have not been correctly assessed in accordance with Clause 63.1 and/or the change to the Completion Date or a Key Date has not been correctly assessed in accordance with Clause 63.3.

The third and fourth circumstances are derived from the need to base an assessment on an Accepted Programme which has been revised as required by Clause 32.

If the Accepted Programme is non-existent or has not been revised as required in Clause 32, the *Project Manager* is required to carry out his own assessment of the programme for the remaining work. This is a major incentive on the *Contractor* to keep his programme up to date.

The *Project Manager* will be motivated to make a fair and reasonable assessment in the knowledge that the *Contractor* may refer the matter to the *Adjudicator*, who may change the assessment.

64.3 This clause provides for the *Project Manager* to have the same time to make his assessment as the *Contractor* was allowed for his.

64.4 This clause (like Clause 62.6) protects the *Contractor* against delay by the *Project Manager* in finalising and implementing quotations for compensation events. Once the quotation is treated as accepted it is implemented (Clause 65.1). The only remedy the Employer then has if he does not agree with the quotation is adjudication.

Implementing **65**
compensation events 65.1 This clause should be read in conjunction with Clause 65.4 for Options A, B, C and D and Clause 65.3 for Options E and F. Implementation is by the *Project Manager* changing the Prices and the Completion Date and/or a Key Date in accordance with the assessment of which he has notified the *Contractor*.

65.2 This clause emphasises the finality of the assessment of compensation events. If the records of resources on work actually carried out show that achieved Defined Cost and timing are different from the forecasts included in the accepted quotation or in the *Project Manager*'s assessment, the assessment is not changed. The only circumstances in which a review is possible are those stated in Clause 61.6.

Main Option clauses

Option A: Priced contract with activity schedule

Assessing compensation **63**
events 63.10 See explanatory notes on core Clause 63.2.

63.12 The changed Activity Schedule (Clause 11.2(20)) which takes account of the effect of the compensation event is used for subsequent assessments of the PWDD.

63.14 It is not always practicable to use the Shorter SCC to assess Subcontractor's costs. This clause permits a sensible alternative should the *Contractor* and *Project Manager* agree.

Implementing **65**
compensation events 65.4 See explanatory notes on core Clause 65.1.

Option B: Priced contract with bill of quantities

Compensation events **60**

60.4 A change in quantity is not, in itself, a compensation event. A compensation event is triggered only by the changed quantity satisfying the two tests stated in the clause.

This clause only applies to changes in quantities which do not result from changes to the Works Information. Subject to the exceptions in Clause 60.1(1), a change to the Works Information is always a compensation event, regardless of the effect on quantities.

60.5 A difference between original and final quantities in a Bill of Quantities is not, in itself, a compensation event. The amount due to the *Contractor* includes the PWDD, which is based on the actual quantities of work done. However, any difference of quantities which causes Completion to be delayed or delays achieving a Key Date is a compensation event.

60.6 There may be mistakes in the Bill of Quantities because the bill does not comply with the *method of measurement* or because of ambiguities or inconsistencies. This may occur where an item has been omitted from the bill or an item in the bill should be deleted or amended to comply with the *method of measurement*. This is one of the compensation events which may result in a reduction of the Prices.

Assessing compensation **63**
events 63.10 See explanatory notes on core Clause 63.2.

63.13 The Bill of Quantities will require amendment in the form of deletion, addition or revision of quantities or items or rates and lump sums. The changes to the Bill of Quantities should be clearly referenced. The changed Bill of Quantities (Clause 11.2(21)), which takes account of the effect of the compensation event, is used for subsequent assessments of the PWDD.

Subject to agreement, the rates and lump sums in the Bill of Quantities may be used for assessing compensation events instead of building up the Defined Cost of each item of work using the SSCC and then adding the Fee. This may apply particularly for small items, where calculations using the SSCC may be unduly lengthy in relation to the value of the compensation event. This method assumes that the rates and prices in the *bill of quantities* are equivalent to Defined Cost plus the Fee.

Implementing **65**
compensation events 65.4 See explanatory notes on core Clause 65.1.

Option C: Target contract with activity schedule

Assessing compensation **63**
events 63.11 See explanatory notes on core Clause 63.2. The proviso in the first bullet is to encourage the *Contractor* to apply value engineering principles to the Works Information.

63.12 The changed Activity Schedule (Clause 11.2(20)), which takes account of the effect of the compensation event, is used for the subsequent calculation of the *Contractor*'s share.

63.15 The Shorter SCC should be useful where there is a large number of small compensation events.

Implementing **65**
compensation events 65.4 See explanatory notes on core Clause 65.1.

Option D: Target contract with bill of quantities

Compensation events 60

60.4 A change in quantity is not, in itself, a compensation event. A compensation event is triggered only by the changed quantity satisfying the two tests stated in the clause.

This clause only applies to changes in quantities which do not result from changes to the Works Information. Subject to the exceptions in Clause 60.1(1), a change to the Works Information is always a compensation event, regardless of the effect on quantities.

60.5 A difference between original and final quantities in a Bill of Quantities is not, in itself, a compensation event. The amount due to the *Contractor* includes the PWDD, which is based on the actual quantities of work done. However, any difference of quantities which causes Completion to be delayed or delays achieving a Key Date is a compensation event.

60.6 There may be mistakes in the Bill of Quantities because the bill does not comply with the *method of measurement* or because of ambiguities or inconsistencies. This may occur where an item has been omitted from the bill or an item in the bill should be deleted or amended to comply with the *method of measurement*. This is one of the compensation events which may result in a reduction of the Prices.

Assessing compensation events 63

63.11 See explanatory notes on core Clause 63.2. The proviso in the first bullet is to encourage the *Contractor* to apply value engineering principles to the Works Information.

63.13 The Bill of Quantities will require amendment in the form of deletion, addition or revision of quantities or items or rates and lump sums. The changed Bill of Quantities (Clause 11.2(21)), which takes account of the effect of the compensation event, is used for the subsequent calculation of the *Contractor*'s share.

Subject to agreement, the rates and lump sums in the Bill of Quantities may be used for assessing compensation events instead of building up the Defined Cost of each item of work using the Schedule of Cost Components and then adding the Fee. This may apply particularly for small items, where calculations using the SCC may be unduly lengthy in relation to the value of the compensation event. This method assumes that the rates and prices in the *bill of quantities* are equivalent to Defined Cost plus the Fee.

63.15 The Shorter SCC should be useful where there is a large number of small compensation events.

Implementing compensation events 65

65.4 See explanatory notes on core Clause 65.1.

Option E: Cost reimbursable contract

Assessing compensation events 63

63.15 The Shorter SCC should be useful where there is a large number of small compensation events.

Implementing compensation events 65

65.3 See explanatory notes on core Clause 65.1.

Option F: Management contract

Implementing compensation events 65

65.3 See explanatory notes on core Clause 65.1.

7 TITLE

Core clauses

For large, expensive or important items of Equipment, Plant or Materials which are being manufactured or stored outside the Working Areas, the *Employer* is advised to secure ownership and at the same time make payment to the *Contractor*. Under Clause 71.1, the *Supervisor* marks such items if the contract identifies them for payment and the *Contractor* has prepared them for marking as required. There are, in consequence, several important procedural steps that need to be taken.

The Works Information must identify the items as being subject to marking under this Section, and other documents such as the *bills of quantities* and *activity schedule* should show them individually and separately. When an *activity schedule* is used, suitable instructions must be included in the instructions to tenderers because it is the tenderer who prepares the *activity schedule*.

When Option C, D or E is used there is the added complication that payment is related to what the *Contractor* has paid or is forecast to pay, not what he has done. Careful drafting of suitable clauses is essential to protect the *Employer*'s position in such cases.

The *Contractor* must prepare the items for marking as required by the Works Information and the *Supervisor* must ensure that these requirements are met.

The *Supervisor* is obliged to mark the items if the criteria of the Works Information have been met.

The requirements in the Works Information for marking should state that, as part of preparing the items, the *Contractor* has to show title and only after demonstration of such title will marking and payment follow. The *Supervisor* must check the title before marking.

Under UK company law it is difficult for the *Employer* to successfully claim title to Equipment that is owned by the *Contractor*. If it is intended that payment is to be made to the *Contractor* for Equipment outside of the Working Areas, then such a payment is best safeguarded by the use of Option X14 in conjunction with a suitable advanced payment bond or by requiring a suitable performance bond using Option X13. If these options are not suitable then the *Employer* should take legal advice on the steps that need to be taken to secure title to any Equipment that is paid for in advance.

In order to simplify matters in such circumstances, the *Supervisor* has the facility to mark Equipment that is outside of the Working Areas if the Works Information requires it. However, title will not pass to the *Employer* for such Equipment by marking alone.

The *Employer*'s title to **70**
Plant and Materials

70.1 Upon the marking of the particular item of Plant or Materials, as separately identified, title passes to the *Employer*.

70.2 Before the *Contractor* removes any items of Plant or Materials (including surpluses and unusable or defective goods) he must obtain the *Project Manager*'s written permission to effect such removal. Not to do so means the items may remain in the title of the *Employer* and hence could cause considerable complications for the *Contractor*, especially if Plant and Materials are returned to suppliers. It would normally be advisable for the *Contractor* and the *Project Manager* to agree a simple procedure in order to facilitate normal movement of resources in and out of the Working Areas.

If the *Project Manager* gives his permission for the removal of Plant and Materials, title in them reverts to the *Contractor*. This may cause problems if Plant and Materials which have been paid for are removed from the Working Areas for work to be done on them elsewhere, such as being returned to the manufacturer for modifications. If this is known to be likely to happen at tender stage, the *Employer* may wish to include a suitable Z clause to safeguard their title. If no such clause is included and the need to remove Plant or Materials happens for an unforeseen reason, the *Project Manager* should ensure that he agrees suitable arrangements with the *Contractor* to safeguard the *Employer*'s position before he gives permission for the Plant and Materials to be removed from Site.

Marking Equipment, Plant and Materials outside the Working Areas **71**

71.1 The procedures necessary prior to marking having been completed to the *Supervisor*'s satisfaction, he has a duty to mark any Equipment, Plant and Materials outside the Working Areas which are stated in the contract to be paid for before being delivered to Working Areas. The contract (i.e. the Works Information, *activity schedule* or *bill of quantities*) must identify the items for which payment may become due.

Removing Equipment **72**

72.1 This clause requires the *Contractor* to remove Equipment from the Site when it is no longer needed. It may, however, be permitted to remain on the Site either temporarily or permanently if the *Project Manager* allows. Examples are temporary storage of items of Equipment pending transfer to another site and temporary sheet piling or formwork which the *Contractor* may not wish to recover. Items such as the latter, however, remain as Equipment left in the *works* and do not become part of the *works*.

On termination, the *Contractor* is not automatically entitled to remove the Equipment from Site if it is still needed to Provide the Works. Under certain circumstances the *Employer* is entitled on termination to use Equipment owned by the *Contractor* in order to complete the works – see Clause 92.2 P3. Once this Equipment is no longer needed by the *Employer* to Provide the Works the *Contractor* removes it from the Site.

Objects and materials within the Site **73**

73.1 This clause establishes that the *Contractor* has no title to objects of value or of historical or other interest within the Site. Title to such objects may belong to the *Employer* or some other party. Any instructions to deal with such objects issued by the *Project Manager*, such as removal to the *Employer*'s store, is a compensation event under Clause 60.1(7).

73.2 The Works Information should state which materials from excavation and demolition are to be the property of the *Contractor* and any conditions regarding their removal from the Site. Note that this clause reverses the 'traditional' approach, which is that the Contractor owns the materials that arise from demolition and site clearance.

The Works Information should state also how the *Contractor* is to deal with known items of value in property to be demolished or elsewhere on the Site and appropriate items included in the *activity schedule* or *bill of quantities* (if any).

8 RISKS AND INSURANCE

Core clauses

It is important to recognise the distinction between the various types of risk and which party bears them. Risks of loss of or physical damage to property or of personal injury or death, which are usually insurable risks, are quite separate from general, legal or financial risks.

Section 8 deals with the general, legal and the insurable risks of loss, damage, injury or death and what insurances are required to cover them. The risks which could result in loss, damage, injury or death, if they happen, are allocated to either the *Employer* or the *Contractor*.

Financial risks are dealt with in other parts of the contract, such as under the compensation event procedure in Section 6. For example, the *Employer* carries the financial risk for additional work instructed under Clause 60.1(1) but, for priced Options A and B, the risk in carrying it out remains with the *Contractor*. In addition, the Employer carries the financial risk if any events that are at his risk occur – see Clause 60.1(14).

On the other hand, under Option A and B the *Contractor* carries the financial risk of doing work which he has priced in the contract. Under Options C and D most of this financial risk is initially the *Employer*'s but is subsequently shared with the *Contractor* under the *Contractor*'s share arrangements in Clause 53. Under Options E and F the *Employer* carries most of the financial risk of carrying out the *works*.

Employer's risks **80**

80.1   The *Employer*'s risks are stated in Clause 80.1. There are six main categories of *Employer*'s risks.

The first is the *Employer*'s risks relating to his use of the Site or *works*, his own general or legal responsibilities and faults in his design. For liabilities which might arise from design faults the *Employer* should either insure the risk by a professional indemnity policy if the design is by his own resources or ensure that it is covered (e.g. under the NEC Professional Services Contract) if an external consultant is engaged to do the design work.

The second category, relating to items supplied to the *Contractor*, is at the risk of the *Employer* up to the point of their handover to the *Contractor* or a Subcontractor. Any insurance cover for these should be either under the *Employer*'s own loss or damage policy or the insurances of Others (as defined in Clause 11.2(10)) until the *Contractor* or Subcontractor has received and accepted the Plant and Materials concerned.

The third category of *Employer*'s risk is the loss of or damage to the *works*, Plant and Materials caused by outside influences beyond the control of the Parties. This risk is limited to what can be regarded as the *Employer*'s property. The *Contractor* carries the risk of loss of or damage to his property, including Equipment from any of these causes.

The fourth category of *Employer*'s risk is that arising once he has assumed responsibility for (i.e. taken over under Clause 35) completed work. Upon this happening, the *Employer* takes on the consequences of normal ownership, including wear and tear, and therefore should insure his asset in the usual way if he so wishes. There are some important risks which, even after take over, remain with the *Contractor*, but these are likely to be small and disappear with the issue of the Defects Certificate.

The fifth category of *Employer*'s risk is that of loss of or damage to the *works* and any Equipment, Plant and Materials retained on the Site after termination.

The last category of the *Employer*'s risks provides for him to carry additional risks. These must be clearly stated in the Contract Data. An important example of where the *Employer* might wish to carry an additional risk or limit the *Contractor*'s risk is when the *works* are within an existing plant or facility of the *Employer*.

For example, in a refinery it is quite usual for the *Employer* to retain all or most of the risk of loss or damage to his property which surrounds the *works* being carried out. In this case the *Contractor* would see from the Contract Data part one to what extent the *Employer* has retained this risk and hence what residual risk he has to insure under the third item in the Insurance Table. If the *Contractor* and the *Employer* in effect share a risk then the *Contractor* must ensure that his insurances are adequate, at least up to the limit of his risk.

Another example would be for equipment made available to the *Contractor* by the *Employer* for which the *Employer* preferred to retain direct control and hence risk. A vital distinction must then be recognised between the equipment which concerns the *Employer* and the Equipment (note the capital 'E' for Equipment in the second classification of insurance in the Insurance Table) as defined in Clause 11.2(7). Thus the risk of loss of or damage to equipment under this example is an *Employer*'s risk but loss of or damage to defined Equipment is a *Contractor*'s risk.

The *Contractor*'s risks **81**

81.1   The *Contractor*'s risks are defined as all the risks which are not identified in Clause 80.1 as being carried by the *Employer*. The *Contractor*'s risks include those as stated in the insurance clauses even when such risk is covered by insurance procured by the *Employer*. This aspect is explained more fully in the explanatory notes for Clause 87.2.

Repairs **82**

82.1   The *Contractor* is required to carry out all works of repair until the Defects Certificate has been issued. Consequently, unless otherwise instructed by the *Project Manager*, this will include repairs arising from an *Employer*'s risk event, such as damage to the *works* after take over but before the Defects Certificate. The carrying out of such work will be a compensation event – see Clause 60.1(14).

The *Project Manager* must therefore decide how to deal with loss or damage caused by an *Employer*'s risk event. It is possible that, in certain circumstances, he decides the damage should not be repaired, or should be repaired by the *Employer* or others employed by him. In such a case he would issue instructions to the *Contractor*, who will then neither be obliged to carry out such repair work nor be entitled to receive any compensation.

Indemnity **83**

83.1   Under this clause each Party indemnifies the other for events which are at his risk.

83.2   Provision is made for the liability of a Party to be reduced on a proportional basis if events at the risk of the other Party contributed to the event.

Insurance cover **84**

84.1   This clause requires the *Contractor* to take out insurance cover. Major multi-discipline employers may prefer to arrange all or some of this insurance themselves in view of the large number and size of contracts in which they invest. In such cases, insurers are likely to take a much greater interest in the running of the contract as the *Contractor* is no longer motivated to minimise claims. If the *Employer* wishes to effect his own insurance, the details should be given in the Contract Data. Otherwise, the events and extent of cover to be effected by the *Contractor* are as shown in the Insurance Table and detailed in the Contract Data.

The *works* and Equipment would normally be insured under a Contractor's All Risks (CAR) policy. Since the value of the *works* constructed will increase as the contract progresses, either the insured sum should be updated at intervals or the policy should recognise such increase as being automatically covered. Insurance of the *works* and Equipment covers only the *Contractor's* risks. It is for the *Employer* to decide whether or not he wishes to take out insurance cover for his own risks. It is important in all cases to check that the terms of any standard policy comply with the requirements of the contract.

Insurance of the *works*, Equipment, and Plant and Materials is on a value indemnity basis. This is particularly relevant to insurance of Equipment as it means that cover is for replacement with equipment of similar age and condition rather than on a 'new-for-old' basis.

With regard to the fourth event in the Insurance Table, employers in many countries are required by law to insure employees for personal injury and death.

The *Contractor* carries the risk for any design that he is required to carry out, and he will often carry Professional Indemnity (PI) insurance for such risks, either directly or through the designers he employs. However, under the ECC he is not required to take out PI insurance, either in his own name or in joint names. The *Employer* may decide that, in the event of the *Contractor* being unable or unwilling to bear the costs caused by his defective design, the lack of such insurance is an unacceptable risk to carry. In that case the *Employer* should include in the Contract Data a requirement for the *Contractor* to take out suitable PI insurance.

84.2   The *Project Manager* and the *Contractor* must ensure that the policies and certificates are in the joint names of the *Employer* and the *Contractor* including for those insurances procured by the *Employer* for those matters at the *Contractor's* risk.

It is important to note that the insurances in the Insurance Table only cover for events which are at the *Contractor's* risk. Thus, whilst the insurances run until the Defects Certificate is issued, the *Employer* assumes most of the risks for the works once they are taken over and therefore the *works* will not be covered by this insurance.

Insurance policies   85

85.1   The *Project Manager* should satisfy himself that the terms of the insurance policies satisfy the contract requirements and that the *Employer's* interests are adequately protected.

If the *Project Manager* is a not an expert in insurances he may need to consult an insurance expert or refer the matter to the *Employer's* insurance department.

85.2   The purpose of waiver of subrogation rights is to prevent insurers taking action against the *Employer's* personnel, for example after having paid money to the *Contractor* in settlement of a claim by him.

85.3   The Parties must comply with the terms of the insurance policies as not so to do may make the insurance partially or fully void and incur the Parties in substantial risk. It is therefore important that the *Project Manager* is aware of any terms that may affect, or be affected by, the actions of the *Employer*.

85.4   This clause is referring in particular to 'deductibles'. Deductibles, often also known as 'excesses', represent the amount of liability retained by the insured. By this means, the insured shares the exposure to risk with the insurer.

The amount of the deductible affects the level of premium which the insured must pay. Reasons for applying deductibles in insurance policies include

- decrease in level of premiums,
- elimination of administration costs of processing a large number of small claims,

- involving the insured in retaining some liability by sharing the risks and thus encouraging him to take more care in avoiding loss or damage, and
- reducing the risk assumed by the insurer to a limit which he can bear.

If the *Contractor* does not insure **86**

86.1   This clause enables the *Employer* to take out the relevant insurances in the event that the *Contractor* fails to do so at the time and for the periods stated in the contract. Appropriate adjustments are then made to the amounts certified by the *Project Manager*.

Insurance by the *Employer* **87**

87.1   In certain circumstances it may be more appropriate and convenient for the *Employer* to effect some of the joint name insurances which, under the standard conditions of contract, are to be taken out by the *Contractor*. The *Contractor* is required to accept the policies and certificates, in the same way that the *Employer* is required to do so for insurances effected by the *Contractor*.

The Employer sets out details of the insurances that he is going to effect, including the deductibles applicable. If in doubt, the *Employer* should discuss the level of deductibles with potential tenderers before completing the Contract Data.

Entering 'nil' or very low amounts against the deductibles in the Contract Data will normally not be in the *Employer*'s best interests because the premiums will be very high. Conversely, high levels of deductibles may lead tenderers to seek to insure all or part of the deductible amount, and either increasing their bid to cover additional premiums or qualifying their tender if they are unable to obtain suitable additional cover.

Tenderers will do this because the insured risks are *Contractor*'s risks and therefore the *Contractor* will bear the cost of the deductibles regardless of who effects the policies.

87.2   Whilst the *Contractor* is entitled to rely upon the *Employer* providing the insurances as stated in the Contract Data, it is important that the *Contractor* recognises that his risks include those shown in the Insurance Table. Consequently, even if such insurances are effected by the *Employer*, the *Contractor* should satisfy himself as to the adequacy of the policy and cover. The *Contractor* should inform the *Project Manager* of any discrepancy between the *Employer*-provided insurances as stated in the Contract Data and the *Employer*-provided insurances as actually given and ask for a policy amendment.

87.3   If the *Employer*

- fails to effect the insurances which the Contract Data states he is to provide, or
- provides insurances which do not comply with the Contract Data,

the *Contractor* may procure additional insurance to top up any shortfall he considers exists in these insurances. The *Employer* will then either pay the insurers directly or the *Contractor* will be reimbursed.

9 TERMINATION

Core clauses

This section describes the circumstances under which the Parties may terminate the contract and the subsequent procedures.

Termination 90

90.1 Both the *Employer* and the *Contractor* have rights to terminate the *Contractor*'s employment. The Party wishing to terminate initiates the procedure by notifying the *Project Manager* and giving his reasons for terminating. If satisfied that the Party giving notice has provided reasons which are valid under the contract, the *Project Manager* issues a termination certificate promptly.

It is important to note that these clauses confer rights on to the Parties, but it is not mandatory that those rights are exercised.

90.2 Only the *Employer* has a right of termination entirely at his discretion, i.e. without one of the reasons listed in Clause 91 as R1 to R21. The *Contractor* can terminate only for one of the reasons listed in the Termination Table. Reasons are given identification references (R1 to R21) for convenience and are fully described in Clause 91. If the *Employer* wishes to terminate for a reason other than those in R1 to R21, he should state this in notifying the *Project Manager* under Clause 90.1.

The procedures to be followed and the amount due to the *Contractor* are generally functions of the reasons for terminating, although some are independent of the reasons.

90.3 The procedures to be followed on termination are given in Clause 92.

90.4 Details of the amounts to be paid to or by the Contractor after termination are given in Clause 93 in conjunction with the Termination Table. The *Project Manager* is required to carry out his assessment of the amount due so that he can certify the final payment within thirteen weeks. The *Employer* pays the *Contractor* any sums certified by the *Project Manager* within three weeks of them being certified; if the sum is due to the *Employer* from the *Contractor* the same time limit applies.

Reasons for termination 91

91.1 The reasons set out in 91.1 deal with the bankruptcy of either Party. The terminology of bankruptcy law varies from country to country. The terms used in this clause are those current in English law, but the clause allows for their equivalents in other jurisdictions. Termination may follow the bankruptcy, etc., of either the *Contractor* or the *Employer*.

The exercise of the right to termination when either Party is faced with the bankruptcy, receivership or administration of the other is not mandatory. For example, it is often in the best interests of the *Employer* when first hearing of the appointment by the *Contractor* of a receiver, administrator or liquidator to discuss with them the possibility of the *Contractor* completing the works or being able to novate the contract to a third party such that work can continue with a minimum of disruption.

91.2　The four week period of grace is provided so that the *Contractor* has the opportunity to correct the default. Notification should be issued to the *Contractor* and usually copied to the *Employer*. If after four weeks the *Contractor* has not corrected the default, the *Project Manager* would, by implication, need to advise the *Employer* of the position so that the *Employer* can exercise his right if he wishes. The *Contractor* may have started to make amends but not fully corrected the default after the four week period. In this case, the *Employer* needs to decide whether or not he wishes to proceed to termination.

Reason R11 applies only to a substantial breach of the *Contractor*'s obligations. Minor breaches are insufficient grounds for the serious step of termination, as a matter of policy.

The bond in Option X13 and the guarantee in Option X4 are both to be provided within stated times. This clause effectively extends those periods by four weeks. No time limits are given for providing an advanced payment bond under Option X14. However, since this bond is provided as security against the advanced payment, delay in providing the bond merely delays the advanced payment to the *Contractor*, which is sufficient sanction.

Subcontracting of work before acceptance by the *Project Manager* (R13) is a breach of Clause 26.2. However, the right to termination only arises when substantial work is subcontracted before acceptance of the Subcontractor.

It is important to note that, whilst the *Project Manager* should bring to the *Employer*'s attention a default that the *Contractor* has not put right within four weeks, it is for the *Employer* to decide if he wishes to terminate the *Contractor*'s employment because of this default. For example, in the case of a breach of Clause 26.2, the *Employer* may decide, after consultation with the *Project Manager*, that the Subcontractor is capable of carrying out the works.

91.3　Both of these reasons include the word 'substantially' for the reason that minor defaults of this nature would not be sufficient grounds for termination. The right to termination for a breach of a health or safety regulation is in addition to any sanctions under the applicable law.

91.4　Late payment entitles the payee to interest under Clause 51.2. Right to termination, however, only arises if payment is delayed beyond thirteen weeks after the date of the certificate and, under R16, the right belongs only to the *Contractor*.

91.5　Rights to terminate under the law (R17) may be a result, in some jurisdictions, of force majeure or frustration.

91.6　These reasons apply to instructions which relate to substantial or all work. Again, judgement is needed to interpret what constitutes substantial work. Procedures and payment depend on which Party was responsible for the default which led to the instruction. R20 provides for an instruction which resulted from the default of neither Party.

91.7　This reason is in effect recognition of a possible effect of force majeure. The event will have been notified under Clause 16 and, once recognised as satisfying the criteria set out in Clause 19, it will have been managed by the *Project Manager*. The *Employer* now has the option to terminate if the event will prevent completion of the *works* or is forecast to delay it by more than thirteen weeks.

A delay to planned Completion which can (as opposed to will) be recovered by acceleration, by increased resources, or by adjusting the programme does not stop the *Contractor* from completing on time. The *Contractor* must demonstrate that there is no reasonable means by which he can complete the *works* on time for the event to be recognised under the second bullet point.

Note that initially the event may have been notified as a compensation event under Clause 60.1(12), (13) or (14), and only recognised as a 'force majeure' event when the *Project Manager* and the *Contractor* considered how to deal with it.

Procedures on termination **92**

92.1 This clause provides flexibility to the *Employer* on termination to decide how and if the works are to be completed. It applies irrespective of the terminating party or the reasons for the termination.

Once the termination procedures are completed, the *Contractor's* employment is terminated and he is no longer allowed access to or use of the *works* or the Site.

92.2 Under procedure P2, the *Employer's* right to enforce assignment of the benefits of a subcontract will be subject to the terms of the subcontract. In certain cases, a new contract (novation) may be necessary.

Procedure P3 is particularly useful to an *Employer* where there is substantial falsework or other major temporary works. However it can only apply to Equipment that the *Contractor* has title to. Equipment which is being hired by the *Contractor* or which is owned by a subcontractor cannot be dealt with in this way unless the *Contractor* has obtained title of it. In that case the *Employer* could use Procedure P2, if available. Otherwise he will be required to negotiate with the Equipment's owner for its continued use.

Title to any Equipment retained by the *Employer* remains with the *Contractor*. The Employer is only allowed to use the Equipment to provide the *works* and cannot retain it for other use or to sell or dispose of it once he no longer needs it. The *Contractor* is required to remove from Site any Equipment retained by *Employer* once it is no longer required to complete the *works*.

Payment on termination **93**

93.1 The amounts listed in this clause (A1) are due whatever the reason for termination.

When paying the Defined Cost for Plant and Materials care must be taken to ensure that there is no duplication with any amount that is assessed as being due for normal payments.

Defined Cost that the *Contractor* has reasonably incurred in expectation of completing the work should include costs which the *Contractor* can show have not been recovered within the normal amount due. For example, for Option A it would include amounts for the work done to the date of termination on activities which were not completed at that time.

Amounts retained by the *Employer* that should be repaid to the *Contractor* on termination are only those amounts that are to be temporarily retained under the contract. They would include, for example, retention (if Option X16 is used) or the amount retained under Clause 50.3 because the *Contractor* has not submitted his first programme. They do not, however, include amounts that are meant to be permanently paid by the *Contractor* to the *Employer*, for example the amount payable under Clauses 25.3 or 45.1, which would be deducted as part of the assessment of the amount due for normal payments.

93.2 The applicability of these amounts (A2 to A4) depend on the particular grounds of termination (see Termination Table). Generally, where termination occurs because of the *Contractor's* default, the *Contractor* is not reimbursed the cost of removing his Equipment. He must also pay the *Employer's* additional costs for completing the *works*, representing at least some of the damages which the *Employer* suffers arising from the *Contractor's* breach of contract.

Main Option clauses

Options C: Target contract with activity schedule

93.4 On termination the *Contractor* is paid or pays his share for the work he has carried out before termination. This is calculated by comparing the Price for Work Done to Date with the total of the Prices for work carried out before termination.

For this calculation there are specific rules defining how to assess the Price for Work Done to Date and the total of the Prices.

Options D: Target contract with bill of quantities

93.5 On termination the *Contractor* is paid or pays his share for the work he has carried out before termination. This is calculated by comparing the Price for Work Done to Date with the Total of the Prices for work carried out before termination.

For this calculation there are specific rules defining how to assess the Price for Work Done to Date.

DISPUTE RESOLUTION – OPTIONS W1 AND W2

Dispute resolution

The ECC has two forms of dispute resolution, Options W1 and W2. The *Employer* should choose and list in the Contract Data part one the Option he wishes to use.

The standard ECC Option is W1. Option W2 has been specifically introduced to be used only when the contract is carried out in the United Kingdom and is a 'construction contract' within the definitions in Sections 104 to 106 of the Housing Grants, Construction and Regeneration Act 1996. If the *Employer* is in any doubt as to whether or not their contract comes within those definitions he should take further legal advice.

These explanatory notes will first deal with the overall principles of dispute resolution in the ECC, which are common to both Options. They will then deal with and comment upon each Option on a clause-by-clause basis, without further repetition of those main principles. A comparison of many of the clauses in the two Options will show that they have common provisions and some are identically worded. However, for convenience, where comments are common between the Options they will be repeated rather than merely referring the reader to the explanatory notes for the other Option.

The only means of dispute resolution in many forms of contract used to be arbitration or litigation, which in recent years had become both time consuming and expensive. Whilst the ECC system recognises the need to have an ultimate means for such final resolution, it introduces an intermediate stage of independent dispute resolution in the form an adjudication. The intention is that all disputes are first referred to, and decided by, the *Adjudicator*, who is jointly appointed by the *Employer* and the *Contractor* and is able to act independently of them.

Following the success of adjudication in previous versions of the ECC the right to adjudication in most forms of construction contracts became mandatory in the United Kingdom with the Housing Grants, Construction and Regeneration Act 1996. Unfortunately, some of the requirements of this legislation are not compatible with the principles of adjudication set out in the ECC, hence the need for a separate Option (W2) for those contracts governed by this Act.

The *Adjudicator*

Under the ECC it is intended that the *Adjudicator* is named by the *Employer* in part one of the Contract Data and appointed before the *starting date*. However, he takes no part in the project unless a Party refers a dispute to him. Checks should be made for any conflicts of interest before naming the *Adjudicator* or proposing a replacement. The *Adjudicator* should always be a named person and not an organisation of firm.

The Parties appoint the *Adjudicator* using the NEC Adjudicator's Contract, which is one of the standard forms in the NEC family of contracts. This sets out matters such as the terms of payment of the *Adjudicator* for his services and his duties, liabilities, etc. His fees are shared equally between the Parties to the dispute regardless of his decision, unless otherwise agreed.

The contract with the *Adjudicator* should be entered into before the *starting date*. This allows any dispute to be referred to the *Adjudicator* quickly, without having to go through the procedure of appointing him. Where the *Adjudicator* is not named in the Contract Data, has not been appointed, or is unable, for whatever reason, to deal with the dispute, each Option sets out the procedure for appointing a replacement adjudicator, who can then decide any existing disputes that his predecessor had not dealt with.

The relevant experience, qualifications and general ability of any prospective adjudicator must be carefully considered. The qualities of the *Adjudicator* should, as a minimum, include

- knowledge of the procedures in the ECC,
- a full understanding of the roles of the *Project Manager* and the *Supervisor*,
- a full understanding of how construction costs arise and how they are affected by changes to plan,
- knowledge of construction planning and of how plans are affected by changes,
- the ability to obtain technical assistance when his own technical knowledge does not cover the matter in dispute,
- the ability to obtain up to date information about construction costs when he does not have access to relevant cost data, and
- an appreciation of construction risks and how allowances for them should be set.

The adjudication

Each Option sets out when and how a dispute may be referred to the *Adjudicator*, and the period that he has to reach his decision. The *Adjudicator* can only decide the dispute referred to him. He cannot, without the agreement of the Parties, decide other disputes that he may be aware of but which have not yet been referred to him by a Party.

The *Adjudicator* has wide powers to ensure that he can properly manage the process of adjudication and resolve the dispute referred to him. He is also free to carry out whatever investigations he considers necessary to enable him to make his decision. However, he should tell the Parties the results of those investigations and invite them to comment before making his decision.

The *Adjudicator* may review any action or inaction of the *Project Manager* or *Supervisor*, and decide what action should have been taken in accordance with the contract. If he decides in the *Contractor*'s favour but it is too late for the action or inaction to be implemented, he will deal with the matter by deciding the effect on the Prices and Completion Date using the same assessment procedure that is used for compensation events.

The decision of the *Adjudicator* may simply be that the *Project Manager* or *Supervisor* should have acted or should not have acted, but in certain circumstances he may also decide what action should have been taken. In the cases in which he decides that the *Project Manager* or *Supervisor* acted or did not act in accordance with the contract or in any other matter which he decides in the *Contractor*'s favour, he assesses both financial and time effects.

In other circumstances, it may be appropriate for the *Adjudicator* to change the disputed action or inaction. For instance, where the *Contractor* disputes the existence of a Defect, which has been notified by the *Supervisor*, the *Adjudicator* may decide in the *Contractor*'s favour. If so, the *Contractor* would be relieved of any obligation to correct, if corrective work has not started. If the alleged Defect has been 'corrected', the *Adjudicator* would decide on the financial and time effects. However, as in other instances, should the *Project Manager* still require additional or remedial work then he may instruct such work as a change to the Works Information. This would be a normal compensation event.

If the *Adjudicator* decides that further sums are due to the *Contractor*, he will normally decide when those are to be paid, and can also award interest on them under Clause 51.3.

If the *Adjudicator* disagrees with the *Project Manager*'s assessment of delay to the Completion Date, he will overrule the *Project Manager*'s decision and the Completion Date will be set in accordance with what the *Adjudicator* decides.

The *Adjudicator* is required to give the Parties reasons for his decision. However, no details are given in the Options of how this decision and its associated reasons are to be drafted. The essential requirement is that the Parties can understand why the *Adjudicator* has reached his decision and can implement it immediately. It may also be subject to careful scrutiny, particularly by a Party who may be dissatisfied with the decision.

In his decision the *Adjudicator* should state the precise nature of the dispute referred to him. The decision might comprise the *Adjudicator*'s opinion on, for example, what the *Project Manager*'s decision should have been in accordance with the contract. It might include assessment of a compensation event, what money is payable by one Party to the other or what changes to the programme are required.

The latter point may cause difficulty since it is likely that the programme has been revised since the events which gave rise to the dispute took place. For instance, there may have been concurrent delays and subsequent delays. Thus the decision should be the effect of the relevant event upon the Completion Date, assessed at the time of the event. The Parties will then be able to take account of this decision in further revisions of the programme.

Other matters which, for completeness, should be included in the *Adjudicator*'s decision are

- details of the contract,
- details of the appointment of the *Adjudicator*,
- circumstances leading to the reference,
- the procedures followed by the *Adjudicator*, and
- information upon which the decision is based.

Where the Parties submit contradictory facts or legal submissions, the *Adjudicator* should summarise the arguments submitted to him, and then state his decision clearly, giving his reasons. These reasons should show how they led to the decision reached.

Submission of a dispute under either of the Options does not entitle any Party to cease activities. The *Adjudicator*'s decision is binding and must be implemented. It can only be changed by a subsequent decision of the *tribunal*, or by agreement between the Parties. Should the *Adjudicator*'s decision change an action or inaction and the *Project Manager* is of the opinion that his or the *Supervisor*'s original action or inaction remains necessary for the completion of the *works* then, subject to it being limited to a change in the Works Information, he is free to further instruct the *Contractor*. A change in the Works Information under these circumstances is a compensation event, as are all such changes.

Review by the *tribunal*

Once the *Adjudicator* has reached his decision the Parties put it into effect. If both are satisfied with the decision, that is the end of the matter. If either Party is not satisfied with the *Adjudicator*'s decision, they have a short period to notify the other of their dissatisfaction, in which case the matter can be dealt with, at any time in the future, by the *tribunal*.

The *tribunal* makes a final and binding decision on the dispute, subject only to any appeals procedure allowed under the applicable law. It is important to note that a dispute cannot be referred to the *tribunal* unless it has first been referred to (and in the case of Option W2 decided by) the *Adjudicator*.

An important feature of the ECC is that the *Employer* is given a choice of tribunal and hence is required in the Contract Data to insert his choice, e.g. arbitration, expert determination, a disputes resolution panel or the courts. However, if arbitration is available under the *law of the contract* (Clause 12.2) it is strongly recommended that arbitration is chosen as the *tribunal*. The rationale for arbitration remains important particularly for disputes upon technical matters for which an arbitrator experienced in the technical context of the dispute is preferable to the courts.

The *tribunal* has wide powers to settle the dispute and is not tied to any decision or action of the *Project Manager* or *Supervisor*. The referral of the dispute to the *tribunal* should not be seen as an appeal of the *Adjudicator*'s original decision. Therefore, either Party may rely upon new evidence and submissions at the *tribunal* that were not put before the *Adjudicator*.

If the *tribunal* is arbitration, the arbitration procedure is that stated in the Contract Data. Such procedure generally deals with appointment of arbitrators and replacement arbitrators and time limits. A number of countries have their own standard arbitration procedures.

If the chosen arbitration procedure does not provide for the appointment and replacement of the arbitrator, the *Employer* should include the necessary procedures in the Contract Data.

In defining those procedures, the following aspects of arbitration should be included.

- On matters of procedure the power of decision should be given to the arbitrator and not the Parties or their legal representatives once appointed.
- The arbitrator should have certain qualifications which should include

  - appropriate training,
  - the ability to manage an arbitration,
  - qualification in the area of the dispute,
  - qualification in the law of arbitration,
  - available time for the arbitration, and
  - the ability to take an active role in the process.

- As far as possible, the exchange of written statements, including experts' reports, should apply.
- The arbitrator must ensure that experts know that their primary duty is to the arbitrator and not to the Parties.
- A limited timetable should be defined for oral hearings, with equal sharing of time between the Parties.
- Case-management conferences at specified stages of the arbitration should be arranged in order to monitor time and expenditure.
- The arbitration needs to take into account any other specific requirements peculiar to the particular project or its expected disputes.

In the United Kingdom, the Institution of Civil Engineers and the Joint Contracts Tribunal publish standard arbitration procedures. Please check with the relevant body for the latest version.

Arbitration procedures frequently used both inside and outside the United Kingdom are

- Rules of Conciliation and Arbitration of the International Chamber of Commerce,
- United Nations sponsored UNCITRAL rules, and
- The ACP/EEC Conciliation and Arbitration Rules, covering contracts funded by the European Development Fund.

Option W1

This is the standard ECC Option and should be used for all contracts except those in the United Kingdom which are regulated by the Housing Grants, Construction and Regeneration Act 1996.

The *Adjudicator* W1.2 (2)   The obligation of impartiality is fundamental to the role of *Adjudicator*. The duty is repeated in the NEC Adjudicator's Contract. The *Adjudicator*'s status is different from that of an arbitrator.

(3)   When the *Adjudicator* has not been named in the Contract Data, this clause describes the procedures and time limits for appointing one. The procedure also applies where a replacement adjudicator is needed in the event that the named *Adjudicator* is unable to act. The *Employer* should name the *Adjudicator nominating body* in the Contract Data part one.

In accordance with the Parties' basic obligations under core Clause 10.1 they are required to try to agree the *Adjudicator*, if one is not named in the contract, or a replacement if the *Adjudicator* is unable or unwilling to act. If they are unable to agree a choice then either Party may ask the *Adjudicator nominating body* to choose and that choice becomes the *Adjudicator*.

The *Adjudicator nominating body* named in the Contract Data would normally be a professional institution or organisation with the ability to appoint a suitable person to act as adjudicator within the timescales set out in the contract.

(4)   An existing dispute on which the original *Adjudicator* has not made a decision is automatically referred to the replacement adjudicator. It is important that the Parties ensure that the replacement adjudicator receives all relevant information. The times stated in the contract for the supply of information and making the decisions then runs from the time of appointment of the replacement adjudicator.

(5)   This clause protects the *Adjudicator* and his employees and agents from possible claims from the Parties. It repeats a provision in the NEC Adjudicator's Contract.

The adjudication W1.3 (1)   This clause sets out in the Adjudication Table the procedure and timetable for the referral of various types of dispute to the *Adjudicator*.

The first item in the table deals with a disputed action of the *Project Manager* or *Supervisor* and the second item deals with their lack of action. The third item deals with the situation that may occur under Clauses 62.6 or 64.4 whereby failure on the part of the *Project Manager* to properly administer the assessment of a compensation event in accordance with the contract may lead to a *Contractor*'s quotation being treated as accepted. Under this item, if the *Employer* disagrees with the quotation, he may refer it to the *Adjudicator*, but only within the time limits stated. The fourth item deals with all other disputes.

The action in dispute under the first item may be, for example

- an instruction,
- an acceptance, non-acceptance or rejection,
- a certification,
- an assessment,
- a notification,
- a decision.

Each instruction, acceptance, non-acceptance, rejection, certification, assessment, notice or decision is a separate action.

In the event of a dispute on an action or lack of action, the dispute may be, for example

- an action which should not have been taken,
- the lack of an action which should have been taken,
- an action taken outside the specified time limits,
- an action which is incomplete or ill-judged,
- an action which is an assessment improperly made or incorrectly calculated,
- an action taken without authority.

For a general matter in dispute, either Party may submit it to the *Adjudicator*. For matters concerning an action or lack of action by the *Project Manager* or *Supervisor*, only the *Contractor* is permitted to submit it to the *Adjudicator*. This is because at all times the *Project Manager* and *Supervisor* are acting on behalf of the *Employer*. The only exception to this is the third item in the table, concerning a dispute about a *Contractor*'s quotation that has been treated as being accepted because of the default of the *Project Manager*, in which case only the *Employer* may refer the dispute.

The initial period of two weeks after the *Contractor*'s notification gives the *Project Manager* or *Supervisor* the opportunity to take or amend the action. This period of grace is intended to prevent the *Adjudicator* becoming involved with matters which may have been overlooked.

(2)   Time stipulations are clearly set out in the Adjudication Table in order to avoid protracted exchanges and argument and to achieve prompt resolution of disputes. However, some disputes can be complex and the times stated may be inappropriate. In that case, and in other cases where the Parties are continuing to negotiate a settlement of the dispute, they should agree to extend the periods set out in the table.

The final sentence of this clause makes the time periods set out in the Adjudication Table, or subsequently extended, time-barring. If they are not met, the Parties loose the right to refer the disputed matter to the *Adjudicator*, and also, because of Clause W1.4(1), to the *tribunal*.

(3)   It is important that the *Adjudicator* has all the relevant information to enable him to reach his decision. The Party referring the dispute is required to include full information about the dispute. The other Parties are required to submit all of their information within a further four weeks, or such other longer period as may be decided by the *Adjudicator*.

(4)   Where a dispute which affects work which has been subcontracted arises, and which may constitute a dispute between the *Contractor* and a Subcontractor as well as between the *Contractor* and the *Employer*, there is provision for the matter to be resolved between the three parties by the main contract *Adjudicator*. This saves time and expense and prevents a dispute being dealt with by different adjudicators who may make different decisions.

This procedure is only possible if the terms of the subcontract permit the *Contractor* to submit the subcontract dispute to the main contract *Adjudicator*.

(5)   The *Adjudicator* has wide powers to manage the adjudication and ensure that he has all of the information he needs to reach a fair decision on the dispute within the time limits set out in the contract. The *Adjudicator* must ensure that he uses these powers fairly and reasonably.

(8)   This clause sets out the period in which the *Adjudicator* may reach his decision, and the circumstances under which it can be extended.

In complex disputes, and for other valid reasons, the *Adjudicator* may require a period greater than the four weeks stated. For example, the *Adjudicator* may require time to visit the Site and may need to consult with other people to help him in arriving at his decision. Consequently, whilst the extension of this period requires the agreement of the Parties, it is recommended that any extra time sought by the *Adjudicator* should be allowed.

(10)   The *Adjudicator*'s decision is binding upon the Parties and they are contractually obliged to act upon it. If they fail to do so it can usually be enforced in the courts, in the same way, and to the same extent, as any other contractual obligation.

The *Adjudicator*'s decision becomes final as well as binding on the Parties if neither of them notifies the other within the time set out in Clause W1.4(2) that he is dissatisfied with it and intends to refer it to the *tribunal*. Note this timescale only applies to the notification of intention to refer and not to the referral itself, which can, and normally will, take place later.

(11)   Once the *Adjudicator* has made his decision and notified it to the Parties his role in the dispute would normally be over. This clause gives him the right to subsequently correct any clerical errors or any ambiguities within a limited period. However, it does not enable him to change any important parts of his decision or the reasons and it cannot be used to re-open the decision.

Review by the *tribunal* W1.4
(1)   A dispute cannot be referred to the *tribunal* unless it has first been referred to the *Adjudicator*. If the *Adjudicator* does not decide the dispute, either at all or within the timescales in Clause W1.3(8), the remedy for either Party is to ask the *tribunal* to decide the dispute, but they only have a limited period to do so – Clause W1.4(3).

(2)   The effect of this clause is time-barring. If either Party is dissatisfied with the *Adjudicator*'s decision they have a short period to notify the other of their dissatisfaction. If neither Party does so within that period, the *Adjudicator*'s decision becomes final as well as binding and it can no longer be referred to the *tribunal*.

The stated period is only for the notification of dissatisfaction. The dispute can be, and normally is, referred to the *tribunal* at a later date.

(3)   The effect of this clause is time-barring. If the *Adjudicator* does not decide the dispute within the time period set out in Clause W1.3(8) then either Party has a further four weeks (from the date that the decision should have been given) to notify the other that they intend to refer the dispute to the *tribunal*. If neither Party does so within that period, the dispute cannot be referred to the *tribunal*.

The stated period is only for the notification of the intention to refer the dispute to the *tribunal*. The dispute can be, and normally is, referred to the *tribunal* at a later date.

Option W2

This Option should only be used in the United Kingdom, and then only if the contract is a 'construction contract' within the definitions in Sections 104 to 106 of the Housing Grants, Construction and Regeneration Act 1996 (the 'Act'). If the *Employer* is in any doubt as to whether or not their contract comes within those definitions he should take further legal advice.

Dispute resolution W2.1
(1)   The phrase 'at any time' is a requirement of the Act. The only practical limit to this time is any limitation period applicable to the contract, either as a requirement of the *law of the contract* or by the application of Clause X18.5. This means that disputes arising several years after the *Contractor* has completed his work may be submitted to the *Adjudicator*.

(2)   In Option W2 and the Act, time periods for adjudication are in days, which means that 'day' must be defined. The definition in this clause is as in the Act. It is important to note that days include Saturdays and Sundays.

The *Adjudicator* W2.2
(2)   The obligation of impartiality is fundamental to the role of *Adjudicator*. The duty is repeated in the NEC Adjudicator's Contract. The *Adjudicator*'s status is different from that of an arbitrator.

(3) When the *Adjudicator* has not been named in the Contract Data, this clause describes the procedures and time limits for appointing one. The procedure also applies where a replacement adjudicator is needed in the event that the named *Adjudicator* is unable to act. The *Employer* should name the *Adjudicator nominating body* in the Contract Data part one. In the United Kingdom there are several adjudicator nominating bodies who are able to appoint a suitable person as *Adjudicator,* including the Institution of Civil Engineers, which keeps a list of suitably qualified persons for this role.

In accordance with the Parties' basic obligations under core Clause 10.1 it will always be better for the parties to agree the *Adjudicator*, if one is not named in the contract, or a replacement if the *Adjudicator* is unable or unwilling to act. However, the Act requires that the contract has a procedure to ensure that an *Adjudicator* is appointed within seven days. This clause, along with Clause W2.3(1), ensures that that timetable can, in all circumstances, be met by a party wishing to refer a dispute to adjudication.

(4) Any existing disputes on which the original *Adjudicator* has not made a decision are automatically referred to the replacement adjudicator. It is important that the Parties ensure that the replacement adjudicator receives all relevant information. The time stated in the contract for the supply of information and making the decision then runs from the time of appointment of the replacement adjudicator.

(5) This clause protects the *Adjudicator* and his employees and agents from possible claims from the Parties. It repeats a provision in the NEC Adjudicator's Contract. It is also a requirement of the Act.

The adjudication W2.3
(1)

The Party wishing to refer the dispute for adjudication initiates the procedure by giving a notice to the other Party, with a copy to the *Adjudicator.* The procedure also confirms or otherwise whether the *Adjudicator* is able to proceed with the adjudication

If the *Adjudicator* is, for whatever reason, unable to decide the dispute within the time period in the contract then he should resign. If the *Adjudicator* does not notify the Parties within three days that he is able to decide the dispute, either Party may act as if he has resigned. In either event the Parties can either agree a replacement adjudicator or either Party can ask the *Adjudicator nominating body* to appoint one in accordance with Clause W2.2(3).

The time periods in this Clause and Clause 2.2(3) are, when aggregated, designed to ensure that a Party can, in any event, have an adjudicator appointed within seven days, as is required by the Act.

(2) This clause sets out the timetable for referral of the dispute to the *Adjudicator,* which is a requirement of the Act. It also sets out the timetable for any further submission by the other Parties to the dispute.

It is important that the *Adjudicator* has all the relevant information to enable him to reach his decision. The Party referring the dispute is required to include full information about the dispute. The other Parties are required to submit all of their information within a further fourteen days, or such other longer period as may be decided by the *Adjudicator*. These periods are stipulated to assist the *Adjudicator* in reaching his decision within the time limits set out in Clause W2.3(8).

(3) Where a dispute which affects work which has been subcontracted arises, and which may constitute a dispute between the *Contractor* and a Subcontractor as well as between the *Contractor* and the *Employer,* there is provision for the matter to be resolved between the three parties by the main contract *Adjudicator.* This saves time and expense and prevents a dispute being dealt with by different adjudicators who may make different decisions.

This procedure is only possible if the terms of the subcontract permit the *Contractor* to submit the subcontract dispute to the main contract *Adjudicator*. In addition, because of the time limits required by the Act it is not practical to refer a subcontract dispute at the same time as a dispute under the main contract without the co-operation of the Subcontractor. For these reasons this clause requires the agreement of the Subcontractor before it can be implemented.

(4) The *Adjudicator* has wide powers to manage the adjudication and ensure that he has all of the information he needs to reach a fair decision on the dispute within the time limits set out in the contract. The *Adjudicator* must ensure that he uses these powers fairly and reasonably.

(5) It is important that any delay caused by one Party does not delay, or stop altogether, the adjudication. Therefore, where either party does not comply with any instructions of the *Adjudicator* the adjudication continues. This would also apply if a Party refused to take any part in the adjudication.

(8) This clause sets out the period in which the *Adjudicator* must reach his decision, and the circumstances under which it can be extended. It complies with the Act.

In complex disputes, and for other valid reasons, the *Adjudicator* may require a period greater than the twenty-eight days stated. For example, the *Adjudicator* may require time to visit the Site and may need to consult with other people to help him in arriving at his decision. Consequently, whilst the extension of this period requires the agreement of one or both of the Parties, it is recommended that any extra time sought by the *Adjudicator* should be allowed.

(10) If the *Adjudicator* fails to make his decision and notify it to the Parties within the timescales required in Clause W2.3(8) he is in breach of his contract with the Parties. In that case the Parties can agree with the *Adjudicator* a revised timescale. Alternatively, either Party may treat the *Adjudicator* as having resigned by procuring the appointment of a replacement adjudicator under Clause W2.2(3).

(11) The *Adjudicator*'s decision is binding upon the Parties and they are contractually obliged to act upon it. If they fail to do so it can usually be enforced in the courts, in the same way, and to the same extent, as any other contractual obligation.

The *Adjudicator*'s decision becomes final as well as binding on the Parties if neither of them notifies the other, within the time set out in Clause W2.4(2), that he is dissatisfied with it and intends to refer it to the tribunal. Note this timescale only applies to the notification of intention to refer and not to the referral itself, which can, and normally will, take place later.

(12) Once the *Adjudicator* has made his decision and notified it to the Parties his role in the dispute would normally be over. This clause gives him the right to subsequently correct any clerical errors or any ambiguities within a limited period. However, it does not enable him to change any important parts of his decision or the reasons and it cannot be used to re-open the decision.

Review by the *tribunal* W2.4 (1) A dispute cannot be referred to the *tribunal* unless it has first been decided by the *Adjudicator*. If the *Adjudicator* does not decide the dispute, either at all or within the timescales in Clause W2.3(8), the remedy for either Party is to appoint a replacement adjudicator using Clauses W2.3(10) and W2.2(3).

(2) The effect of this clause is time-barring. If either Party is dissatisfied with the *Adjudicator*'s decision they have a short period to notify the other of their dissatisfaction. If neither Party does so within that period, the *Adjudicator*'s decision becomes final as well as binding and it can no longer be referred to the *tribunal*.

The stated period is only for the notification of dissatisfaction. The dispute can be, and normally is, referred to the *tribunal* at a later date.

SECONDARY OPTION CLAUSES

Option X1: Price adjustment for inflation (used only with Options A, B, C and D)

In the case of Options A, B, C and D, the *Employer* should decide how the risk of inflation is to be allocated. If he decides to accept all of this risk himself, he should include Option X1. Without Option X1, the allocation of the risk of inflation depends upon which main Option is used, as follows.

- For Options A and B the contract is firm price and the *Contractor* carries all of the risk of inflationary increases in the costs of labour, plant, materials, etc.
- For Options C and D the risk of inflation is initially borne by the *Employer* as he pays recorded Defined Costs, which are effectively 'current costs'. The risk is subsequently shared with the *Contractor* through the application of the calculation for *Contractor*'s share, Clause 53.

For cost reimbursable and management contracts (Options E and F), the *Employer* already carries all of this risk since payments are of recorded Defined Cost. These are 'current costs' and automatically include for price increases occurring since the contract was signed. Option X1 is therefore irrelevant to Options E and F.

Defined terms   X1.1   The source of the published priced indices to be used should be identified in part one of the Contract Data together with the proportions of the total value of the *works* to be linked to the index for each category. Allowance is made for a non-adjustable portion which represents the portion for which the *Contractor* carries the risk of inflation. The total of the proportions should be one.

Also entered in the Contract Data is the *base date*, which should normally be four to six weeks before the latest date for submitting tenders.

One of the effects of the calculation is that the non-adjustable element in the formula affects the amount of payment for price adjustment made for compensation events. For example, if a compensation event is assessed some time before the work is done, the *Contractor* does not recover the non-adjustable element on the increased costs for the period between the assessment and when the work is eventually paid for. This is similar in principle to the effect of the non-adjustable element on originally tendered work, namely that the *Contractor* does not recover the non-adjustable proportion from the time when the tenders were prepared until the work is paid for. The effect is not penal provided the non-adjustable element is kept to a small proportion of the total factor. A maximum of 10% is reasonable.

If a compensation event reduces the amount of work to be done, the effect is opposite and the deduction from the Prices is less than the full amount according to the proportion of the non-adjustable element.

Price Adjustment Factor   X1.2   Quite often, provisional index figures are published which are corrected to final figures at a later date. The first part of this clause requires re-calculation using final figures where these are different from provisional figures.

The second part of this clause has the effect of freezing the Price Adjustment Factor at the Completion Date for the whole of the *works*, thus requiring the *Contractor* to carry the risk of inflation of the cost of work done after this date. It should be noted that the Completion Date is the date by which the *Contractor* should finish the *works*, not the date when he actually finishes it.

If there are sectional Completions (Option X5), the effect of this clause is that if earlier *sections* are finished late but before the last Completion Date, the *Contractor* will be paid price adjustment on late work. This is part of the ECC system in order to avoid the difficulties of subdividing payments after a *section* has been completed and subdividing the calculation as between work contributing to various sectional Completions. This could be a complex and contentious calculation.

In the extreme case of a relatively small amount of work having to be done well after the main body of the work, the main body of the work becomes exposed to inflation payments if late simply because there is a small volume of work to be done later. The ECC has a means of avoiding this problem which should be borne in mind when preparing a contract. This is to exclude the small amount of work from the definition in the Works Information of work which has to be done before Completion. If this is done, inflation adjustment will freeze even though this work will not be completed.

Compensation events X1.3

Under Clause 63.1, compensation events are assessed on the basis of Defined Cost of work already done and forecast Defined Cost for future work. Defined Cost is assessed using the Shorter SCC (for Options A and B) or the SCC plus the payments to Subcontractors (for Options C and D) in conjunction with the Contract Data, where appropriate. The result is that, in the general case, some Defined Cost will be in current terms (money of the day) and some will be in *base date* terms – where rates for employees and Equipment are stated in the Contract Data. This clause reduces current Defined Cost to *base date* levels so that changes to the Prices for compensation events (Clause 63.1) are made in *base date* terms. When assessments of the amount due are made, the Price for Work Done to Date will be adjusted for inflation under Clause X1.4 or Clause X1.5.

If Option X1 is not selected, compensation events are still assessed using Defined Cost, which, in the general case, will be a mixture of current costs and *base date* costs. Tenderers will need to consider the amount of contingency for the inflation rate that they wish to include in the rates for the SCC or Shorter SCC stated in the Contract Data.

Price adjustment Options A and B X1.4

'Each amount due' is the total to date and only the changes in the amount due are certified after each assessment date (Clause 51.1). Thus the total of the three bullet points listed in Clause X1.4 represents the total amount in respect of price adjustment up to the date of each assessment.

Example

Assume the increase in the Price for Work Done to Date in the assessment is £5,000 and the Price Adjustment Factor (PAF) is 0.05 (i.e. 5% inflation since the *base date*). The calculation for the first bullet point in Clause X1.4 is

$$£5,000 \times 0.05 = £250$$

The sum of £250, plus the total of the sums resulting from the same calculation in previous assessments, plus any correcting amount resulting from the third bullet point, is the amount for price adjustment included in the amount due.

Price adjustment Options C and D X1.5

Adjustment for inflation for target contracts is necessary for the calculation of the total of the Prices (Option C) or Total of the Prices (Option D), which is only used to calculate the *Contractor*'s share and not the periodic payment of the amount due. This arises because the Price for Work Done to Date is the Defined Cost plus the Fee. Defined Cost is current cost and automatically includes any inflation occurring since the *base date*. However, since the *Contractor*'s share is calculated from the difference between the total (Option C) or Total (Option D) of the Prices and the Price for Work Done to Date, the two must be compatible in terms of allowance for inflation. The total of the Prices for Option C is derived from the Activity Schedule, and the Total of the Prices for Option D is derived from the Bill of Quantities. It is these which must be adjusted for inflation.

The first of the two bullet points in Clause X1.5 determines the inflationary component of the increase in the Price for Work Done to Date since the last assessment.

Example

Assume the increase in the Price for Work Done to Date for the assessment is £5,000 and the Price Adjustment Factor is 0.05 (i.e. 5% inflation since the *base date*). The calculation for the first bullet point in Clause X1.5 is

$$\text{PWDD}\left(1 - \frac{1}{1+\text{PAF}}\right) = \frac{\text{PWDD} \times \text{PAF}}{1+\text{PAF}}$$

i.e. $\quad \dfrac{5,000 \times 0.05}{1.05} = 238.10$

The sum of £238.10, plus any correcting amount resulting from the second bullet point, is the price adjustment amount for the assessment and is added to the total (or Total) of the Prices. The result of this calculation at each assessment is added to the total (or Total) of the Prices to maintain comparability with the final Payment for Work Done to Date.

Option X2: Changes in the law

Changes in the law **X2**

X2.1 This clause removes from the *Contractor* the risk of changes in the law which occur after the Contract Date. In certain countries, such changes can have a dramatic effect on the *Contractor*'s costs and on his ability to make progress to complete the *works* on time. Only changes which affect the *Contractor*'s costs are included. Thus changes of law affecting the following examples are not compensation events

- income tax or any other tax paid by employees,
- corporation tax or any other charges on profits.

Changes of law affecting the following examples would be compensation events

- employment tax paid by the *Contractor*,
- import duties,
- customs payments.

For the purposes of this clause, law would include a national or state statute, ordinance, decree, regulation (including building or safety regulations) and a by-law of a local or other duly constituted authority or other delegated legislation.

The *Contractor* may notify the *Project Manager* of a compensation event under this Option, using the procedure in core Clause 61.3. He is most likely to do this when a change in the law has the effect of increasing the cost to him of Providing the Works. However, the clause is reciprocal in the sense that the *Employer* gains the benefit of a change in the law which reduces costs.

Option X3: Multiple currencies (used only with Options A and B)

Multiple currencies X3

Provision for multiple currencies in Options C and D is made in Clause 50.6 and in Options E and F in Clause 50.7. Therefore this clause is only used with Options A and B.

This Option is used when it is intended that payment to the *Contractor* should be made in more than one currency and that the risk of *exchange rate* changes should be carried by the *Employer*. It is based on the procedure used by the World Bank on development funded projects. The effect is that the *Contractor* is protected from the currency *exchange rate* changes which may take place after a fixed date as they affect designated parts of the work.

If an item is to be paid for by the *Employer* in the *currency of the contract* and the *Contractor* chooses to pay for it, or part of it, in another currency, the *Contractor* carries the risk of changes in the *exchange rate*. Payment to the *Contractor* is not affected.

If, however, the total of the Prices at the Contract Date, which will be expressed in the *currency of the contract*, includes items identified as to be paid by the *Employer* to the *Contractor* in another currency, the *Employer* takes the risk of any movement in the *exchange rate* after the date of the published *exchange rates* stated in the Contract Data. This is achieved by listing the items in the Contract Data and fixing the *exchange rate* to be used for each currency relative to the *currency of the contract*. This ensures that the *Contractor* is paid the amount of the other currency which he has quoted for the item.

Option X3 with Option X1

When Option X3 is used in a contract which also includes Option X1, and if an index used in the formula for price adjustment is local to the Site, published in the country of the Site, and covers materials which are normally imported to that country, the index will take account of currency *exchange rate* variations between the supplying country and the importing country. Any such materials should not also be covered by the multiple currency arrangement in Option X3, otherwise a double compensation for *exchange rate* variation will result.

If an index used in the formula is an index published in the country or origin of a commodity it will not reflect changes in currency *exchange rates* between the country of origin and the country to which the commodity is being supplied. It is then appropriate, if Option X3 is used, to include this commodity in the list of items for payment in a second currency in order to protect the *Contractor* from currency *exchange rate* variations.

X3.1

The *Employer* should state in the Contract Data which items of work are to be paid for in currencies other than the *currency of the contract*, what those currencies are, the maximum amounts payable in each currency, the *exchange rates* to be used in calculating the payments and their date of publication. *Exchange rates* are usually those published some two weeks before the date for submission of tenders.

X3.2

The limits to the amounts payable in each currency should be stated in the Contract Data. Any limit should be set sufficiently high to allow for any additional payments due to compensation events requiring more of any currency than envisaged at the Contract Date. If there is no limit on the amount of the relevant currency, 'no limit' should be entered.

Option X4: Parent company guarantee

Parent company **X4**
guarantee X4.1 Where a parent company guarantee is required by the *Employer*, it should be provided by the Contract Date. If that is not achieved, a four week limit is provided as a fall-back. Failure to provide the guarantee within this period entitles the *Project Manager* to notify the default under Clause 91.2. If the *Contractor* does not provide the guarantee within a further four weeks, the *Employer* is entitled to terminate. The form of the guarantee should be included in the Works Information in part one of the Contract Data. If the *Employer* wishes specific provision for the *Contractor* to price the guarantee separately in his tender, an appropriate item should be included in the *activity schedule* or the *bill of quantities* (if any).

Option X5: Sectional Completion

Sectional Completion **X5**
X5.1 This Option should be included when the Employer requires parts of the works to be completed before the whole of the *works*. The parts are called *sections*, each of which should be identified in the Contract Data part one, with requirements for the work to be done by the *completion date* of each stated in the Works Information.

Once Completion of a *section* is achieved the *Employer* takes over that *section*, see core Clauses 35.1 and 35.3. The *Employer* then assumes the risk for loss, wear, or damage to that *section* of the *works*, with the exception of certain events, see core Clause 80.1. The *Employer* is required to give access to the *Contractor* to any *section* that he has taken over if it is needed to correct a Defect, see core Clause 43.4.

Sectional Completion is best used where the *Employer* wants the *Contractor* to complete a defined physical part of the *works* so that he or another contractor can take over that *section* entirely. Once a *section* is completed and taken over the *Contractor* would not be expected to carry out any other work to that *section*, other than the correction of any Defects.

Examples of *sections* could include the following.

- Completion of a major Plant item for commissioning for the *Employer*'s use ahead of the rest of the *works*.
- Completion of a floor of a multi-storey building so that fitting out by Others can commence.
- Completion of a new access route into the *Employer*'s facilities to enable the existing access route on which part of the *works* are sited to be closed.

On a multi-contract project, the *Project Manager* or *Employer* will often require the *Contractor*'s work to have achieved a defined Condition by a certain date, without necessarily being complete. In that case it will be better to define that Condition by using a Key Date. Examples of where Key Dates, rather than sectional Completion, should be used include the following.

- The *Contractor*'s design having reached a defined stage to enable information to be passed to Others so that their design can proceed.
- A wall having been built to a certain level so that Others can start to fix their plant to it.
- Completion of some, but not all, of the *works* on a floor of a multi-storey building so that Others can commence their work, which is to be carried out at the same time as the remainder of the *Contractor*'s work on that floor.

Further explanation of Key Dates, with examples, is given in the explanatory notes to Section 1.

Completion of the *sections* is followed by Completion of the whole of the *works*. However, it is not necessary to define a *section* for all parts of the *works*. Any parts of the *works* that are not defined within a *section* are required to be complete when the whole of the *works* is complete.

When defining *sections* to be completed earlier than the whole of the *works*, thought must be given to how the *Employer* or Others can gain access to that *section*. If access is needed through parts of the *works* that have not yet been taken over, this will require careful and full explanation in the Works Information.

Each *section* has a *completion date*, either stated by the *Employer* or tendered by the *Contractor*. Delay damages and bonus for early Completion can be related to the sectional Completion Dates by using Options X7 and X6, respectively.

Completion of a *section* of the *works* does not affect the *defects date*, which is defined by reference to Completion of the whole of the *works*. Likewise, where Option X16 is used, the dates when retention is released are not affected by early Completion of a *section* of the *works* as they are defined by reference to Completion of the whole of the *works* and the issue of the Defects Certificate.

Option X6: Bonus for early Completion

Bonus for early Completion **X6**

X6.1   Where Completion as early as possible would benefit the *Employer*, whether of the *works* or of a *section* of the *works*, the *Employer* can use this Option to motivate the *Contractor* to achieve early Completion. The bonus calculated in accordance with this clause will be included in the assessment occurring at Completion, or at the first assessment date after the date when the *Employer* takes over the *works*.

Option X7: Delay damages

Delay damages **X7**

X7.1   Delay damages are liquidated damages paid by the *Contractor* if he fails to complete the *works* by the Completion Date. It is recommended that this Option is included in most contracts. Under English law and some other legal systems, if it is not included, delay damages are 'at large' and the remedy open to the *Employer* if the *Contractor* fails to complete the *works* by the Completion Date is to bring an action for damages for the *Contractor*'s breach of contract. In this event, evidence of the actual damages suffered by the *Employer* is required.

The amount of delay damages should not exceed a genuine pre-estimate of the damage which the *Employer* will suffer as a result of the *Contractor*'s breach. They are described as delay damages in the NEC family of contracts as these are not the only liquidated damages. Others are low performance damages (Option X17) and interest for delayed payments in core Clause 51.2.

Appropriate entries for delay damages should be made in the Contract Data. They may comprise loss of rent, loss of profit from a manufacturing facility, costs due to delayed start of another contract, or simply interest on the capital invested in the project for the period during which the *Employer* has been deprived of its benefit. The *Employer* is advised to keep a record of the calculation. Damages greater than a genuine pre-estimate constitute a penalty and are not generally enforceable under English law.

If Option X7 is used and no entry or a 'nil' entry is made in the Contract Data, it is likely that the *Employer* will be unable to recover any damages if the *Contractor* fails to complete the *works* by the Completion Date.

It is also emphasised that, if Option X7 is included, the deduction of delay damages once they become due is part of the assessment made and certified by the *Project Manager* (Clause 50.2). They are not deducted by the *Employer* from the *Project Manager*'s certified amount due.

If Option X7 is used in conjunction with Option X5 for sectional Completion, an estimate of delay damages should be stated in the Contract Data against the Completion Date for each *section*. A separate entry should be included for delay damages for the whole of the *works*.

Since delay damages are amounts to be paid by the *Contractor*, appropriate deductions are made in the first assessment of the amount due occurring after the Completion Date, and in subsequent assessments up to the earlier of Completion and the date on which the *Employer* takes over the *works*.

If the Parties wish to limit the total delay damages for the whole of the *works*, the entry in the Contract Data should be amended by adding 'with a maximum total amount payable of...'. Similar amendments should be made to the Contract Data if it is intended to place a cap on the damages for particular *sections* of the works where Options X5 and X7 are used together.

X7.2   This clause protects the *Contractor* when he has paid delay damages and a later assessment of a compensation event results in a delay to the Completion Date. This could occur when a compensation event arises at a late stage in the work or if an *Adjudicator* or the *tribunal* changes the assessment of a compensation event and their decision is made after delay damages have been paid. The *Employer* is required to repay any overpayment of delay damages with interest.

X7.3   Under core Clause 35.2, if the *Employer* uses part of the *works* before Completion is certified he is deemed to have taken over that part when he starts using it, unless the take over is for a reason stated in the Works Information or to suit the *Contractor*'s method of working. In that case, the *Employer* has had the benefit of using part of the *works* and it would be unfair to levy the delay damages in the contract applicable to all of the *works* if the *Contractor* subsequently completed the rest of the *works* late. The delay damages are therefore reduced in the proportion that the benefit of the taken over part of the *works* has to the benefit of the whole of the *works*. It is important to note that when calculating this proportion the actual (or assessed) benefits known at the time of the calculation should be used, not those assumed when the delay damages were originally calculated. This proportion is then applied to the original delay damages. This can best be illustrated by the following example.

> The contract is for the construction of a factory to build two types of widgets, types A and B. This has separate buildings with production lines for each type of widget and the *Employer* calculates that he will make £5,000 per day profit out of type A and £3,000 out of type B. He decides that he wants Completion of both buildings to occur together and therefore sets the delay damages at £8,000. However, the *Employer* takes over one of the buildings first and starts making the type A widgets. Meanwhile, the market price of both widgets has changed so that the *Employer* assesses he will make £4,000 out of type A and £5,000 out of type B (total now £9,000).

The proportion of the new benefit of the part of the *works* still to be taken over to the new benefit of all of the *works* is now £5,000/£9,000, i.e. five ninths. This proportion is then applied to the original level of the delay damages to provide the following delay damages for the remaining part of the *works* not yet taken over

$$£8,000 \times 5/9 = £4,444.$$

If Option X5 is used with Option X7, the same principle applies to the delay damages that are applicable to a *section* of the works.

Option X12: Partnering

Partnering X12

A partnering contract, between two Parties only, is achieved by using a standard NEC contract. Option X12 is used for partnering between more than two parties working on the same project or programme of projects. In that case Option X12 should be used as a secondary Option common to the contract which each party has with the body which is paying for its work. The parties who have this Option included in their contracts are all the bodies who are intended to make up the project partnering team. It should be noted however that Option X12 does not create a multi-party contract.

The content of Option X12 is derived from the 'Guide to Project Team Partnering' published by the Construction Industry Council (CIC). The requirements of the CIC document that are not already in the NEC core and main Option clauses are covered in Option X12.

The purpose of Option X12 is to establish the NEC family as an effective contract basis for multi-party partnering. As with all NEC documents, it is intended that the range of application of this document should be wide. Option X12 can be used for

- partnering for any number of projects (i.e. single project or multi-project),
- international projects,
- projects of any technical composition, and
- organisations as far down the supply chain as required.

Parties must recognise that by entering into a contract which includes Option X12 they will be undertaking responsibilities additional to those in the basic NEC contract.

A dispute (or difference) between Partners who do not have a contract between themselves is resolved by the Core Group. This is the Group that manages the conduct of the Partners in accordance with the Partnering Information. If the Core Group is unable to resolve the issue then it is resolved under the procedure of the Partners' Own Contracts, either directly or indirectly with the *Client,* who will always be involved at some stage in the contractual chain. The *Client* may seek to have the issues on all contracts dealt with simultaneously.

Because Option X12 does not create a multi-party contract it does not include direct remedies between non-contracting Partners to recover losses suffered by one of them caused by a failure of the other. Such remedies are available to each Party to the contract (i.e. the *Employer* or the *Contractor*) within the core and main Option clauses, but only for the other Party's failures or the failures of a Partner who is lower down the *Contractor*'s supply chain.

The final sanction against any Partner who fails to act as stated in the Option X12 is for the Partner who employed them not to invite them to partner again.

There are many scenarios in setting up a project. The NEC family of contracts with the Option X12 is sufficiently flexible to deal with them. For example, an initial contract may be a Professional Services Contract with a *Contractor* for a feasibility study. Subsequently that *Contractor* may do later work using the ECC. The *Contractor* may be a Partner during both stages of his contribution to the project.

Additional Contract Data for Option X12

The *Client* is the Party for whom the projects are being carried out. He may or may not be the *Employer* depending upon how far down the supply chain the contract is. The *Client* is named in the Contract Data.

The *Client's objective* is the objective for the 'programme of projects' if more than one or for 'the project' if only one. The *Client's objective* should be expressed quantitatively if possible (the business case). It should also include the partnering objectives.

Partnering Information includes any requirements for

- use of common information systems,
- sharing of offices,
- attendance at Partners' and Core Group meetings,
- participation in partnering workshops,
- arrangements for joint design development,
- value engineering and value management,
- risk management, and
- other matters that the Core Group manages.

This information should not duplicate requirements in the Works Information or other sections of the Contract Data.

The additional Contract Data for the Option, like other Contract Data in the NEC contracts, does not change. The Schedule of Partners and the Schedule of Core Group Members, like the Activity Schedule and other schedules referred to in Contract Data, do change from time to time. The following are samples of the typical information required in these schedules.

Date of last revision: . . . .

The Core Group members are the *Client* and the following.

Name of Partner	Address and contact details	Joining date	Leaving date

Example of Schedule of Core Group Members

Identified and defined terms X12.1 (1) The *Contractor* becomes a Partner when his contract with Option X12 comes into existence. Other participants, including at least the *Employer* and the *Client* (if they are not the same), will already be Partners. Other parties become Partners when their Own Contract (which includes Option X12) comes into existence. They should then be named in the Schedule of Partners and their representative identified.

(3)   Not every Partner is a member of the Core Group.

(5)   There are two options for subcontractor Partners with regards to the payment of bonus/cost associated with a Key Performance Indicator (KPI). Either the amount payable cascades down if the schedule allocates the same bonus/cost to the main contractor and subcontractor, or the main contractor absorbs the bonus/cost and does not pass it on.

An example of a KPI is set out in the explanatory notes for Clause X12.4(1), which follows.

Working together   X12.3 (5)   The Core Group organises and holds meetings. It produces and distributes records of each meeting, which include agreed actions. Instructions from the Core Group are issued in accordance with the Partner's Own Contract. In the case of the ECC incorporating Option X12 they are issued by the *Project Manager* to the *Contractor*. The Core Group may invite other Partners or people to a meeting of the Core Group.

(8)   The Partners should give advice and assistance when asked, and in addition whenever they identify something that would be helpful to another Partner.

(9)   A Subcontractor or consultant that the *Contractor* intends to employ for the project may be a Partner, but the general policy on this should be decided at the beginning of the Project. The Core Group should advise the *Contractor* at the outset if a Subcontractor or consultant is to be asked to be a Partner. The *Contractor* should not appoint a Subcontractor or consultant who the Core Group decides should be a Partner if he is not willing to be a Partner.

Incentives (also 'X12.2 (1) and X12.3(3)')   X12.4 (1)   If one Partner lets the others down for a particular target by poor performance, then all lose their bonus for that target. Therefore, all must work together in partnership to achieve the targets. Targets are not achieved by coercion.

If the *Employer* tries to prevent a target being met, he is in breach of core Clause 10.1.

There can be more than one KPI for each Partner. KPIs may apply to one Partner, to several Partners or to all Partners.

An example of a KPI

KPI	Number of days to complete each floor of the building framework
Target	14 days
Measurement	Number of days between removal of falsework from the entire slab and from the slab below
Amount	Main contractor – £5,000 each floor
	Formwork and concrete sub-contractor – £2,000 each floor
	Structural designer – £750 each floor

(2)   The *Client* should consult with the other Partners before adding a KPI. The effect on subcontracted work should be noted; adding a KPI to work which is subcontracted can involve a change to the relevant KPI for the Subcontractor and/or Subconsultant.

Date of last revision: . . . .

The Partners are the following.

Name of Partner	Representative's address and contact details	Contribution and objective	Joining date	Leaving date	Key Performance Indicator	Target	Measurement arrangement	Amount of payment if the target is achieved or improved upon*

* Enter *nil* in the last column if there is to be no money incentive.

Example of schedule of Partners

Option X13: Performance bond

Performance bond **X13**

X13.1 Option X13 should be used where a performance bond is required by the *Employer*. The *Contractor* should, ideally, provide the bond by the Contract Date. If that is not achieved, a four week limit is provided as a fall-back. Failure to provide the bond within this period entitles the *Project Manager* to notify the default under Clause 91.2. If the *Contractor* does not provide the bond within a further four weeks, the *Employer* is entitled to terminate.

The form of the performance bond should be included in the Works Information and the amount of the bond should be stated in part one of the Contract Data.

For ECC contracts using main Options A or B the Contractor should include the cost of this bond within his tendered total of the Prices. If the *Employer* wishes the *Contractor* to price the bond separately in his tender, an appropriate item should be included in the *activity schedule* or the *bill of quantities*. For all other Options the cost of this bond to the *Contractor* is included within his Fee.

Option X14: Advanced payment to the *Contractor*

Advanced payment **X14**

X14.1 The option of making an advanced payment is intended for contracts in which the *Contractor* has to make a heavy investment at the beginning, for example to buy or mobilise major items of Equipment before construction work starts. The start time for repayment of the advanced payment and the repayment amounts are stated in part one of the Contract Data. It is advisable to set these data so that the advance is fully repaid within the first half of the construction period.

To ensure that an advanced payment is not duplicated, instructions to tenderers should make it clear that, when there is an advanced payment, the *activity schedule* or *bill of quantities* should not be priced to produce another advanced payment. For example, there should not be provision for early purchase of Equipment in the *activity schedule* or method related charges in the *bill of quantities* for equipment purchase if an advanced payment is to be made under this Option.

In entering the amount of the advanced payment in the Contract Data, it should be made clear whether the amount is inclusive or exclusive of VAT or other sales tax. If such tax is payable on amounts to be certified later by the *Project Manager*, it would also be due on the advanced payments.

The advanced payment does not require an assessment to be made or certified by the *Project Manager*. Instead, it imposes an obligation on the *Employer* to pay within the periods set out in X14.2. Some *Employer's* or funding agencies' procedures require the production of a certificate by the *Project Manager* before any payment can be made. If that is the case then the *Project Manager* may need to assess and certify such payment, but that is not a requirement of the contract.

X14.2 This clause allows for the provision of a bond, if required by the *Employer*, as security for the advanced payment. The bond should normally be provided before the Contract Date, but if this is not achieved, the advanced payment can be delayed until not later than four weeks after the *Employer* has received the bond. The form of the bond should be included in the Works Information by the *Employer*. The value of the bond decreases as the *Contractor* repays the advanced payment.

If the *Employer* wishes to make specific provision for the *Contractor* to price the bond in his tender, appropriate items should be included in the *activity schedule* or *bill of quantities* (if any).

If the *Employer* is late in making the advanced payment, the financial consequences for the *Contractor* may be significant. For example, he may be unable to purchase or mobilise the Equipment he needs, which could delay the *works* and lead to him incurring additional costs. Therefore, the normal provision for interest due on late payments (core Clause 51.2) could be inappropriate and it is replaced by the assessment of the effects of the delay in making the advanced payment as a compensation event.

X14.3 The Contract Data should include the minimum number of weeks after the Contract Date after which the first instalment of the repayment of the advanced payment is included in the assessment. If the instalment is an amount, it should be a simple fraction of the amount of the advanced payment.

The advanced payment will normally be made before the first assessment of the amount due by the *Project Manager* (Clause 50.1). Repayment of the advanced payment takes place gradually as part of the certified payments of the amount due. A consequence of this is that the total of the certified payments made to the *Contractor* under the normal assessment procedure will always be less than the total payment (including the advanced payment) made to the *Contractor* when Option X14 is being used. This must always be borne in mind when including payments under the contract in the internal financial statements of the *Employer* and the *Contractor.*

Option X15: Limitation of the *Contractor*'s liability for his design to reasonable skill and care

The *Contractor*'s design **X15**

X15.1 Without this Option the *Contractor*'s liability for his design is strict; that is, it must be in accordance with the Works Information. In English law therefore the *Contractor* would be responsible for ensuring that his design is fit for the purpose stated in or reasonably implied from the Works Information.

Option X15 reduces the *Contractor*'s liability for his design to 'reasonable skill and care'. In any dispute the burden of proof is on the *Contractor* to demonstrate that he used reasonable skill and care, not upon the *Employer* to show that the *Contractor* did not.

X15.2 When a Defect in the *Contractor*'s design is found he is required under core Clause 43.1 to correct it. Without Option X15 the *Contractor* is liable for such a Defect and therefore corrects it. However using Option X15, if the *Contractor* can show that he used reasonable skill and care when designing that part of the *works,* he is not liable for the Defect. He is still required to correct the Defect, but that correction is a compensation event.

Option X16: Retention (not used with Option F)

Retention **X16**

The purpose of retention is to enable the *Employer* to retain a proportion of the Price for Work Done to Date as security and as an additional motivation for the *Contractor* to complete the *works*. It does have an effect on the *Contractor*'s cash flow, which he will make allowances for in his tendered Prices (for Options A and B), or his Fee (for the other Options). However, the procedure used in the ECC has no effect on this cash flow until the Price for Work Done to Date exceeds the *retention free amount* (see Figure 4).

The effect of Option X16 on the *Contractor*'s cash flow will also depend upon the amount of work he subcontracts. The *Contractor* will normally hold an equivalent retention on his Subcontractors, thus improving his cash flow. In order to ensure that there is no double-deduction of retention, the Defined Costs for Options C to F are calculated using the gross payments made to Subcontractors, i.e. before deduction of their retention (see Clauses 11.2(23) and (24)).

Option X16 is not normally required where Option X13 (performance bond) is used.

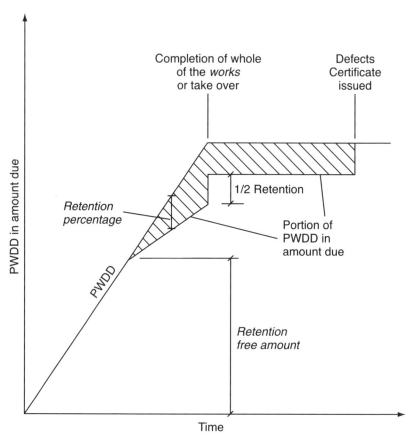

Figure 4. Option X16 – Retention.

X16.1 The *retention free amount* and the *retention percentage* should be entered in part one of the Contract Data. The amount to be retained from the amount due is related to the Price for Work Done to Date only and not to any other sums.

If the *Employer* prefers to use the more conventional method for retention, this can be effected by entering in the Contract Data the required *retention percentage* and 'nil' for the *retention free amount*.

If the Parties wish to limit the maximum amount of retention, the entry in the Contract Data should be amended by adding 'with a maximum total amount payable of...'. This figure can be expressed either as a lump sum or as a percentage of the tendered total of the Prices.

X16.2 Half of the retention being held is released either at Completion of the whole of the *works* or when the *Employer* takes over the whole of the *works*, whichever is earlier. The amount of retention held after this release does not increase or decrease in later assessments until the Defects Certificate is issued.

Four weeks after the date of issue of the Defects Certificate is an assessment date (core Clause 50.1). In this assessment, retention is reduced to zero.

Option X17: Low performance damages

Low performance **X17** If the *Contractor* produces substandard work (a Defect such as low quality
damages brickwork, reinforced concrete or electrical insulation) the *Employer* can

- insist that the *Contractor* corrects the Defect to provide the quality specified in the Works Information (Clause 43.1),
- recover the cost of having it corrected by other people if the *Contractor* fails to correct the Defect within the *defect correction period* (Clause 45.1), or
- accept the Defect and also a quotation from the *Contractor* for reduced Prices, an earlier Completion Date, or both, in return for a change to the Works Information (Clause 44).

Where the performance of the works in use fails to reach a specified level due to a design or other fault of the *Contractor* and the Defect is not corrected so that it is listed in the Defects Certificate, the *Employer* should be able to recover the damages he suffers in consequence. This Option provides for these damages to be recovered as liquidated damages.

The required performance should be specified in the Works Information, e.g.

- the output of an electricity generating station,
- a standard of water quality to be produced by a water treatment plant.

The low performance damages included in the Contract Data should be a genuine pre-estimate of the actual damages that the *Employer* will suffer as a result of the *Contractor*'s breach. Under English law, damages greater than a genuine pre-estimate constitute a penalty and are not generally enforceable.

A convenient method of calculating damages for low performance is the assessment of a lump sum to compensate for the loss of performance over the lifetime of the asset. The forecast net present value of the lost performance over the forecast life of the asset is an appropriate amount.

The amounts of damages are entered in the Contract Data part one against different ranges of low performance. Certification of performance by the Supervisor would follow a specified performance test to be carried out between Completion and the *defects date*.

For example, for a specified performance of an electricity generating station in the Works Information of 100 MW, the entries in the Contract Data could be

- £X000 for performance less than 100 MW but not less than 98 MW
- £Y000 for performance less than 98 MW but not less than 96 MW

continuing down to a 'threshold' performance below which the *works* will be unacceptable to the *Employer* and he would wish to reject them and seek compensation under the general law.

Any deductions of low performance damages are made in the assessment made at the date of issue of the Defects Certificate.

Option X18: Limitation of liability

X18 This Option places limits on various liabilities that the *Contractor* may have to the *Employer* arising under or in connection with the contract. It is particularly relevant to ECC applications in the process plant sector and design and construct contracts generally. It may also be required for international contracts because of the uncertain position which contractors could face in some jurisdictions regarding their liabilities. The Option addresses three key liabilities. It can also provide overall caps, in terms of both time and moneys, beyond which the *Contractor* has no further liability to the *Employer*.

Flexibility has been maintained by the use of amounts stated in the Contract Data for each cap, which can vary from 'nil' to whatever amount the Parties are prepared to accept. If the *Employer* wants to use some, but not all, of the provisions of this Option he can insert the word 'unlimited' against those matters that he does not wish to cap.

Users are advised to seek legal advice relating to the law under which the contract is to be made in order to be aware of how these provisions and the amounts used may be applied under that law.

X18.1 This clause limits the *Contractor*'s exposure to what are commonly referred to as consequential or indirect losses incurred by the *Employer*.

X18.2 In projects where the *Contractor* is required to work within or adjacent to an *Employer*'s existing facility, the *Contractor* is exposed to risks arising from damage he may cause to such a facility. The *Employer*'s costs arising from such an incident could be many times greater than the value of the contract, or of the insurance which either Party may have arranged either under the contract or otherwise. This clause limits the claim the *Employer* may make against the *Contractor* for his costs.

The amount stated in Contract Data would typically be set to something within the amount of cover provided by the insurance if the *Contractor* provides the insurance or closer to the deductible if the *Employer* provides the insurance. However, the *Employer* should check with their insurers first in case the insurer advises the *Employer* to set the amount at a higher level to retain rights of subrogation.

X18.3 The *Contractor*'s liability for his design can be limited to an amount stated in the Contract Data. This liability can also be limited to 'reasonable skill and care' by inclusion of Option X15. Without Option X15, the *Contractor*'s obligation is to design strictly in compliance with the Works Information. In English law, for example, the *Contractor* would be responsible for ensuring that his design is fit for the purpose stated in or reasonably implied from the Works Information.

Clause 45.1 covers the cost of correcting any uncorrected Defects listed in the Defects Certificate. The limited liability for the *Contractor*'s design has effect only for Defects notified after the Defects Certificate has been issued (Clause 43.3).

The term 'design' in the context of engineering and construction contracts is generally interpreted in the broadest sense. It may include not merely structural calculations and the dimensions, shape and location of the work, but also the choice of particular Plant and Materials for particular functions and, similarly, the choice of particular work processes.

X18.4 This clause limits the *Contractor*'s overall liability to the *Employer* to an amount stated in the Contract Data, subject to the exclusions stated. The amount stated should be equal to or higher than the other limiting amounts stated elsewhere in this Option to allow for amounts that may become due to the *Employer* from other rights he may have under the applicable law.

This clause also confirms that the limits apply irrespective of whether the *Employer* is making the claim under the contract, in tort (or delict in some jurisdictions) or in terms of any other right the *Employer* might have under the *law of the contract*.

Amounts payable by the *Contractor* for the listed excluded matters are not included within this limit. However, although loss and damage to the *Employer*'s property is listed as an exclusion, this can, nevertheless, be limited under X18.2.

X18.5 In law the *Contractor*'s liability to the *Employer* may not end when the Defects Certificate has been issued, particularly for a Defect or other matter which only becomes apparent some time after the *defects date*. Such Defects are often referred to as latent defects. Many, but not all, legal jurisdictions have cut-off periods after which the *Contractor* is no longer liable for such latent defects or any other matters under the contract. Clause X18.5 can be used to either reduce the cut-off period set by law or, if none exists, add such a cut-off period.

The *Contractor* is not liable to the Employer for any matter, which would include any Defect, which is notified to him after the *end of liability date*.

Option X20: Key Performance Indicators (not used with Option X12)

Key Performance Indicators **X20** The performance of the *Contractor* can be monitored and measured against Key Performance Indicators (KPIs) using this Option. Their aim is to offer an incentive to the *Contractor* to achieve the *Employer*'s objectives by setting clear measurable targets. These can be related to the *Employer*'s business wide or project specific objectives.

The *Employer* can specify a detailed Incentive Schedule in the tender Contract Data. Alternatively he can set out in the instructions to tenderers the business and project specific objectives that are important to him and invite the tenderers to propose suitable KPIs. Such proposals can then be included in the *Employer*'s tender appraisal. In that case the *Employer* and successful tenderer should agree the Incentive Schedule before the Contract Date.

The intention of KPIs is to encourage, rather than coerce, the *Contractor* to meet the *Employer*'s objectives. Therefore they should only be used as an incentive and not as a penalty. The *Contractor* will be paid a bonus if the target for the KPI is achieved but should not be penalised if it is not achieved.

The principle behind every KPI is that both Parties should benefit when it is met. Therefore, if the KPIs have been correctly chosen, it will be in both Parties' interests to ensure that they are achieved. If the *Employer* tries to prevent a target being met, he will be in breach of Clause 10.1.

Option X20 with Option X12 Option X12 (Partnering) includes KPIs in multi-party arrangements, where the *Employer* wishes to offer incentives to members of the project team. Option X20 can be used to provide incentives when Option X12 is not used. The incentive sharing arrangements in Option X12 are sufficiently flexible to cover the payment of different incentives to different Partners, such that Option X20 is unnecessary in contracts when Option X12 is used.

Identified and defined terms

X20.1 The Incentive Schedule should provide details of the performance that the KPI is intended to measure, how it is to be measured, the target that is to be achieved and the amount to be paid to the *Contractor* if is it achieved. KPIs should be chosen such that they can be objectively measured, thus enabling both Parties to know when they have been achieved. The use of subjective judgements, for example using phrases such as 'reasonable satisfaction' etc., should be avoided.

An example of a multi-party KPI is given in the notes for Option X12. If the Structural Engineer had little input into meeting the target and if the Subcontractor was not a Partner, it could equally be used in Option X20, with only the *Contractor*'s bonus specified.

It would then be the responsibility of the *Contractor* to offer any incentives to his Subcontractors he thinks are necessary to encourage them to help him achieve his target. In Options A and B those incentives would be irrelevant to the *Employer*. With the other Options the *Employer* will share the cost of such incentives, but only to the extent that they meet the requirements of core Clause 52.1.

X20.2 The *Contractor* is required to report at regular intervals his actual past and forecast future performance with regards to the KPIs. The intervals should be sufficiently short such that future performance can be assessed and corrective action taken under Clause X20.3.

X20.3 This clause ensures that problems that will prevent a target being met, and methods to overcome them, are identified as early as possible. This will enable the *Contractor* and *Project Manager* to work together to ensure that the targets are met wherever possible.

However the *Project Manager* can neither accept nor reject the *Contractor*'s proposals, and therefore he cannot coerce the *Contractor* into achieving a target at any cost.

X20.4 The *Contractor* should be paid the bonus in the next assessment following the date he meets his target, see the second bullet of core Clause 50.2. Payments should not be left until Completion.

Payments made to the *Contractor* under Option X20 are not part of Defined Cost or the Price for Work Done to Date. Therefore they are not included in the calculation for the *Contractor*'s share under Clause 53 in Options C and D.

X20.5 The *Employer* may wish to add further incentives to encourage the *Contractor* to meet other objectives. However he cannot remove or reduce any incentive already offered, whether or not it has yet been achieved.

OPTION Y

Option Y(UK)2: Payments under the Housing Grants, Construction and Regeneration Act 1996

Y(UK)2   This Option should only be used for projects carried out in the United Kingdom that are subject to the Housing Grants, Construction and Regeneration Act 1996 (the 'Act').

If the contract is subject to the Act, this Option is incorporated by reference in the Contract Data. It is used to supplement the core clause payment provisions in order to ensure that they comply with the Act. The effect of incorporating this secondary Option is to keep all the payment terms expressly within the contract (see Figure 5) and avoid additional terms being implied by this Act.

The adjudication provisions of the Act are incorporated into the contract by using Option W2 of the disputes resolution procedure.

Y2.1 (2)   In the NEC family of contracts, periods of time are usually measured in weeks to avoid complications of rest days and statutory holidays. However, to comply with the Act, in this Option time periods are stated in days, using the same definition as in the Act.

Y2.2   In order to comply with Section 110 of the Act, this Clause defines when the payment becomes due and the final date for payment. It also confirms that the *Project Manager*'s certificate, issued under core Clause 51.1, is the notice of payment required by Section 110 of the Act. This certificate needs to show the basis upon which any payment has been calculated.

Y2.3   In order to comply with Section 111 of the Act, this sets out the requirement for a notice of any amount to be withheld and the date by which it is to be issued.

Y2.4   Under Section 112 of the Act the *Contractor* has the right to suspend performance if he is not paid in full the amount due under the contract, i.e. the amount in the *Project Manager*'s certificate, by the final date for payment, unless an effective withholding notice has been issued under Clause Y2.3. If the *Contractor* exercises this right it is a compensation event.

Option Y(UK)3: The Contract (Rights of Third Parties) Act 1999

Y3.1   This Option should be used for all projects carried out in England, Wales or Northern Ireland of where the *law of the contract* is the law of England, Wales, or Northern Ireland.

The Contracts (Rights of Third Parties) Act 1999 allows a third party to a contract, i.e. not the *Employer* or the *Contractor*, to enforce a term of that contract in certain circumstances. This Option will ensure that only those terms that are clearly set out in Part one of the Contract Data can be enforced by those persons, or class of persons, that are named. This will ensure that third party rights cannot be implied from any of the other terms of the contract or Works Information

If the *Employer* wishes to provide such a right to a third party he should take legal advice on the full implications and the words to be used in the Contract Data before doing so.

Option Z: *Additional conditions of contract*

This Option should be used where the *Employer* wishes to include additional conditions. These should be carefully drafted in the same style as the core and optional clauses, using the same defined terms and other terminology. They should be carefully checked for consistency with the other conditions.

Additional conditions should be used only when absolutely necessary to accommodate special needs, such as those peculiar to the country in which the work is to be done. The flexibility of the ECC main and secondary Options minimises the need for additional conditions. Additional conditions should never be used to limit how the *Contractor* is to do the work in the contract as this is part of the function of the Works Information.

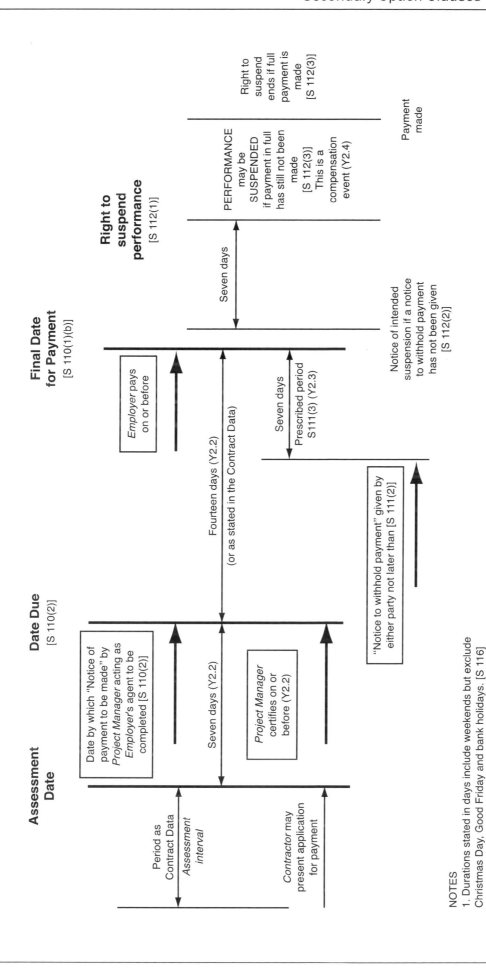

Figure 5. Payment periods when Option Y(UK)2 is used.

NOTES
1. Durations stated in days include weekends but exclude Christmas Day, Good Friday and bank holidays. [S 116]

SCHEDULE OF COST COMPONENTS

General notes

The ECC contains a Schedule of Cost Components (SCC) and a Shorter SCC. This section of general notes applies to both versions of the SCC. It is followed firstly by notes which are specific to the full SCC and then by notes on the Shorter SCC. The term 'full SCC' is not used in the contract but is used in these notes to distinguish it clearly from the Shorter SCC.

Compilation

Matters which have been considered in compiling the SCC are

- the treatment of compensation events in terms of their impact on the costs incurred by Subcontractors (see below),
- the ECC definitions of 'Plant and Materials' and 'Equipment', which differ from those found in most traditional contracts,
- the principle that cost components which are not listed in the SCC are to be covered by the Fee, for which the cost components are not separately listed, and
- the need for greater accuracy when assessing costs which are to be directly reimbursed, as in Options C, D and E, compared with the estimate normally required for a compensation event.

Use of the SCC

The full SCC is part of the contract only when Option C, D or E is used. The SCC

- defines the cost components for which the *Contractor* will be directly reimbursed and
- defines the cost components which are included in an assessment of changed costs arising from a compensation event.

The Shorter SCC is used to define the cost components only when assessing a compensation event. It is always used for this purpose when Option A or B is chosen. If Option C, D or E is chosen, the Shorter SCC may be used in assessing a compensation event if the *Project Manager* and *Contractor* agree or by the *Project Manager* when making his own assessments.

The SCC does not apply to Option F (management contract) where the definition of Defined Cost is restricted to payments due to Subcontractors and suppliers and to the prices for work done by the *Contractor* himself.

For Options A and B the Shorter SCC is a complete statement of the cost components under the definition of Defined Cost, whether work is subcontracted or not.

For Options C, D and E the Defined Cost includes payments due to Subcontractors in addition to the cost components in the SCC for work which is not subcontracted.

Working Areas

The Site is defined as the area within the *boundaries of the site* stated in the Contract Data. This area will comprise locations provided by the *Employer* for the *works*. *Contractor*s often make use of other areas, sometimes adjacent to the Site, for a variety of purposes, such as batching plant, temporary workshops and steel bending yards. On some contracts the *Contractor* may establish depots which are distant from the Site. Where these areas are specific to the contract and closely associated with Site activity, their costs should be included in the SCC rather than covered by the Fee.

In order to achieve this the concept of Working Areas is introduced. The Working Areas include the Site and other areas. It is preferable for the *Contractor* to list in the Contract Data part two specific areas by location. Sometimes the precise area may not be known at tender or it may be anticipated that the area could change during the contract (for example, where the location of an off-site batching plant will be moved during the construction of a road or where the *Contractor* is responsible for locating borrow pits). In these cases a generic description of the purpose or type of area should be listed. In addition, further areas may be added to the Working Areas if the *Contractor*'s proposals are accepted under the procedure in Clause 15.1.

Defined Cost: treatment of Subcontractors

The definitions of Defined Cost vary between main Options to reflect different treatments of the costs of Subcontractors.

Options A and B

The only use of the Shorter SCC is in the assessment of compensation events. Compensation events are assessed as their effect on the *Contractor*'s forecast or recorded Defined Cost. To achieve this satisfactorily, Subcontractors' costs should be available in the same way as the *Contractor*'s costs. All the elements in the Shorter SCC apply equally to the *Contractor* and Subcontractors. Thus payments to Subcontractors are not included in Defined Cost. If they were, the effect would be to remove the Subcontractors' costs from an assessment of compensation events. This would also have the effect of absolving the *Contractor* from all payment risks with respect to Subcontractors.

Under Options A and B, both the *Contractor* and any Subcontractors are required to show the effects of a compensation event on their forecast costs. The *Contractor* and Subcontractor must prove the effects and this will be easier if they give the *Project Manager* access to their accounts and records.

Options C and D

In these Options, compensation events result in an adjustment of the target and the argument used for Options A and B could be applied to target contracts. However, these are contracts with low risk to the *Contractor* and it is intended that the *Contractor* should be protected from payment risks with respect to Subcontractors. Thus payments to Subcontractors are included in Defined Cost for both the assessment of the compensation events and for the calculation of the Price for Work Done to Date. It follows that the *Employer* pays both the *Contractor*'s Fee and the Subcontractor's Fee.

Option E

Cost reimbursable contracts place a very low level of risk on the *Contractor*. As with target contracts the *Contractor* is intended to be protected from payment risks with respect to Subcontractors and payments to Subcontractors are included in the Defined Cost. The *Employer* pays both the *Contractor*'s Fee and the Subcontractor's Fee.

In these contracts there is no tendered price to adjust for compensation events. However, the compensation event procedure is in core and therefore applies to Option E. This is to ensure that *Employers* receive forecasts of the effects of compensation events for budgeting and planning purposes. It also provides a basis for decisions such as whether to proceed with a proposed change to the Works Information.

Option F

The management *Contractor* is intended to be insulated from the cost risk of those subcontracts which he is required to place. This is achieved both in calculating the Price for Work Done to Date and in assessing compensation events by stating that the Defined Cost is the payments due to Subcontractors plus the prices for work done by the *Contractor* himself.

In stating that for Option F, as well as for Options C, D and E, the *Contractor* is protected from payment risks with respect to Subcontractors, it could appear that the *Employer* has no control over risks from Subcontractors. This is not the case as other clauses give the *Project Manager* the right to influence the form of subcontract and the selection of Subcontractors and to disallow payments for compensation events to Subcontractors where these have not been properly assessed in accordance with the terms of the subcontract. When preparing the tender documents for a management contract the *Employer* or his *Project Manager* may wish to include more detailed procedures for the selection and control of Subcontractors. These should be stated in the Works Information.

Where the *Employer* is directly reimbursing Defined Cost he is entitled to

- benefit from all discounts received by the *Contractor*, including any bulk purchase discounts received by head office, and
- pay prices for subcontracted and supplied goods and services which are fair prices obtaining in the open market. For example, the *Employer* is entitled to protection from paying artificial prices for plant hire or road-stone products supplied by *Contractor*-owned subsidiaries.

Clause 52.1 is intended to achieve these aims.

Disallowed Costs	The inclusion of a cost element in the SCC does not necessarily entitle the *Contractor* to payment of all costs incurred. The definitions of Disallowed Cost in Options C, D and E (Clause 11.2(25)) and in Option F (Clause 11.2(26)) identify the circumstances in which costs will be excluded from Defined Cost. These clauses are intended to motivate the *Contractor* to work efficiently and to enable him to be reimbursed for all his costs itemised in the SCC if he does. If he does not work efficiently, for example by ordering materials above the level required to cover loss and wastage, the appropriate costs can be disallowed by the *Project Manager*.
The cost components	If the *Employer* believes that any item in the SCC is not relevant he can delete it for a specific contract. However, an item can still be left in the list even if no costs arise in relation to it.

If there are particular costs which the *Contractor* will have to pay which are not covered (which might be the case on some overseas contracts), the *Employer* can add items to the list when preparing the tender documents. Occasionally it may be appropriate to include in the SCC items presently covered in the Fee.

In part two of the Contract Data there are four groups of entries relevant to the SCC. The first group requires the tenderer to provide data for the Shorter SCC when Option A or B is used. The next three groups are to be completed when Option C, D or E is used and cover data for the full SCC, design data for both schedules and data for the Shorter SCC in case it is used (Clause 63.14).

NOTES ON THE FULL SCC

People 1	Two categories of people are identified whose specific costs can be included as Defined Cost. Items 11, 12 and 13 list the cost components which can be included.

The first category of people excludes *Contractor*'s staff who are working, for example, at head office. Their costs must be allowed for within the Fee, as is normal practice on reimbursable contracts.

The second category deals with *Contractor*'s staff and labour who are required to work temporarily within the Working Areas. This may, for example, be on work which was unplanned at tender but has arisen due to a compensation event.

12   If the *Employer* wishes, the full SCC may be amended for a particular contract by replacing items 12(c) and (d) by more specific components. Examples include payments for

- working at height,
- working in exposed conditions,
- trades supplements,
- plus rates,
- shift allowances,
- tool allowances,
- local allowances, and
- food allowances.

13   Item 13(i) could also be made specific if required. Examples include payments by the *Contractor* for

- taxes in respect of employees,
- National Insurance contributions,
- payments under employment law,
- levies for industrial training (if required by law), and
- employer's liability insurance.

The full SCC need not be more specific unless it is judged that a dispute is likely if a specific item is not defined. If it is judged necessary to define one specific item, then all other items which would fall under items 12(c) and (d) and 13(i) should also be defined.

14   For people on the *Contractor*'s payroll, wages and salaries will be included. For people not on the payroll, the amount paid by the *Contractor* will be included. In dealing with a third party who supplies labour only (often known in the United Kingdom as the 'gangmaster') it is difficult or impossible to gain access to the sort of records or accounts needed to justify the wages and any other payments made to the labour force. As a result the *Contractor* has only to justify the amount he has paid the supplier of the labour.

Equipment   2   Equipment covers *Contractor*'s materials, fuels and other consumables, scaffolding, machinery, testing equipment, transport, construction plant, temporary works, and all types of accommodation including cabins, workshops and laboratories, etc. It may also include accommodation for the *Employer* which the *Contractor* is required to provide. However, for simplicity, the full SCC treats some 'Equipment', such as tools, survey instruments, computers and laboratory equipment, as an overhead under the 'Charges' section.

The full SCC covers the following.

21   Equipment hired from sources external to the Contractor or his parent company.

22   Equipment owned by the Contractor, i.e. purchased from external sources either new or second hand, or purchased from a subsidiary or a member company of the *Contractor*'s parent group.

22   Equipment purchased by the *Contractor* under a hire purchase or lease agreement. This category is included because the question of 'ownership' is legally complex and treated differently under the laws of different countries.

22   Equipment hired by the Contractor from a subsidiary or from a member company of the *Contractor*'s parent group.

For 21 the Defined Cost is the hire cost and includes operators if the item of Equipment is charged by the hirer on an all inclusive basis. If the operators of hired Equipment are shown as a separate charge by hirers then these operators should be costed under the people item, as required by item 28 of the SCC.

For Equipment covered by the three bullets of 22 it is not appropriate for Defined Cost to be the inter-company charge as it is difficult to assess whether internal rates are fair commercial rates. Thus a surrogate 'hire rate' is needed and the options are provided as follows.

- Equipment not listed by the *Contractor* in part two of the Contract Data is dealt with under 22 by establishing open market rates. Generally those items of Equipment for which it is easy to establish market rates would not be listed in the Contract Data.
- The *Contractor* may have Equipment which is non-standard and market rates are difficult to establish. Such Equipment should be listed in the Contract Data so that its cost will be dealt with under 23.
- The change in value approach adopted in 23 may not be suitable for some Equipment, such as an old but effective crane barge for offshore work. Special Equipment should be listed in the Contract Data with the rates to be charged in accordance with 24.

25   Some items of Equipment will be consumed in carrying out the *works*. These include fuels, lubricants, shuttering materials, welding rods and other similar items. For Equipment which is consumed, the Defined Cost is the purchase price.

26   This covers payments to others for work done on Equipment, such as erecting a batching plant or a workshop. If the *Contractor* does this work himself his Equipment and People costs are covered through the relevant section of the SCC.

27   Again if the *Contractor* uses his own Equipment and people to, for example, secure the store's compound, materials purchased separately for this purpose are covered by this clause.

Plant and Materials   **3**   The definition of Plant and Materials (Clause 11.2(12)) makes it clear that a charge to Defined Cost can only be made for those items which are intended to be included in the *works*.

The Disallowed Cost clause in Options C, D and E (Clause 11.2(25)) is designed to deter the *Contractor* from excessively over-ordering Plant and Materials and permit the cost of surplus Plant and Materials to be disallowed after allowing for reasonable wastage. This should be taken into account when assessing Defined Cost under items 31. However, 31 does allow payments for removing Plant and Materials from the Working Areas to be included in Defined Cost. An example of the need for this would be when an item of Plant and Materials is not required due to a change in the Works Information.

The Disallowed Cost clause in Options C, D and E and in Option F (Clause 11.2(26)) also permits costs to be disallowed if a procurement procedure stated in the Works Information has not been followed. This could be particularly relevant to the procurement of Plant and Materials.

32   The change to this clause deals with an unintended outcome of Clause 11.2(25) working in conjunction with this section of SCC when Options C, D or E are used.

Assume the *Contractor* spends £10,000 on materials but has significantly over-ordered. The *Project Manager* disallows £1,000 so the *Contractor* is paid £9,000. He then disposes of the surplus for £500, which in the second edition was credited to cost, thereby reducing cost to £8,500. The *Contractor* would be penalised by £1,500 for a mistake whose real cost was £500.

With the change to the third edition, using the same scenario the *Contractor* is paid £9,000 as a result of the Disallowed Cost but he retains the £500 obtained for the sale of the surplus.

The effect on the *Contractor* is the same if no costs had been disallowed. He would initially have been paid £10,000 but cost would now be credited £500, reducing his payment to £9,500.

The effect on the *Employer* differs. If the cost had been disallowed, the cost to the contract would be £9,000. If the cost had not been disallowed, the cost to the contract would be £9,500.

The change is equitable to the *Contractor* irrespective of whether the cost is initially disallowed or not. The effect on the *Employer* is narrowed as under the second edition the cost to the contract was £8,500 if the cost had been disallowed and £9,500 if it had not been.

Charges: Percentage for Working Areas overheads   44

On reimbursable contracts the items listed under item 44 are usually paid as Defined Cost, although in some contracts they have been treated as overheads and covered by a pre-defined percentage. The percentage is usually applied to the Defined Cost of people, i.e. staff and labour. The latter is administratively simpler and places a little more risk on the *Contractor*, including, for example, the risk of excessive wastage of tools. When the full SCC is used in assessing compensation events the effect on the cost of the items under item 44 would have to be forecast as if they were treated as direct costs. The effort required to do this would be totally disproportionate to their value and there would be a high likelihood of dispute. Consequently they remain as Defined Cost but are treated in a pre-defined way which is common to both target and cost reimbursable contracts and compensation events. The *Contractor* inserts the percentage for Working Areas overheads in part two of the Contract Data when preparing his tender.

Manufacture and fabrication   5

The use of cost reimbursable contracts is not recommended where manufacture and fabrication outside Working Areas forms a major part of a contract. When they have been used in the past, e.g. for defence procurement contracts, they have tended to cause difficulties in the control and identification of Defined Cost.

The SCC is also used for the assessment of compensation events where quotations are based on the effects of the compensation event on Defined Cost. For manufacture and fabrication contracts this creates difficulties which often result in negotiated price changes in the form of lump sums. One of the reasons for the difficulty is that fabrication shop overheads can be several hundred percent of the labour costs.

The use of a percentage for manufacture and fabrication overheads should simplify the administration in both these cases. It is tendered in competition and can be used in assessing tenders in a similar way to the percentage for Equipment depreciation and maintenance.

Item 2 of the full SCC is restricted to Equipment used within Working Areas and therefore equipment, machinery, tools, etc. used in fabrication shops outside the Working Areas must be allowed for in the overheads percentage.

Item 5 excludes the costs of manufacture and fabrication of Plant and Materials which are 'off the shelf'. These are covered by Item 3 of the full SCC.

For Options C, D and E the definitions of Defined Cost, together with the preamble to the SCC, mean that manufacture and fabrication done by the *Contractor*, either within or outside the Working Areas, is paid for at Defined Cost, using the appropriate part of the SCC. However, for manufacture and fabrication done by Subcontractors in these Options, the SCC does not apply irrespective of where the work is done.

Design   6

Components of design costs need to be included in the SCC so that compensation events which affect design costs result in compensation for the *Contractor*. Item 6 is restricted to design done outside the Working Areas. This could have been omitted from the SCC with the effect that such costs are covered in the Fee. However, this would have been unfair on two counts. Firstly because the ECC envisages that a significant amount of design could be done by the *Contractor*, and secondly because consultants' agreements usually provide compensation to consultants for design charges incurred for reasons outside their control.

The costs of designing Equipment are included. As a result the *Contractor* is reimbursed design costs for compensation events which have a significant impact on the design of temporary works.

The policy adopted for design overheads is similar to that for manufacture and fabrication. Consequently the cost of computer facilities, reprographic facilities, etc., is covered by the percentage for overheads.

Insurance 7

The first of these deductions avoids the *Employer* having to pay for costs which the *Contractor* should have insured against. If the *Contractor* does not insure as required by the contract then such costs are at his own risk. (Also see Clause 85.4.)

The second deduction ensures that the *Contractor* does not receive double payment as a result, for example, of insurance which he has voluntarily taken or from insuring for a greater cover than required by the contract.

If the *Employer*'s insurers make payments of other costs incurred by the *Contractor* (because the event is an *Employer*'s risk – see Clause 80.1) then it would be appropriate to allow the *Contractor*'s costs to stand against Defined Cost but the *Employer* will be able to meet those costs from the payments from his insurers.

The Fee

All costs not included in Defined Cost are treated as included in the Fee (Clause 52.1), which should also allow for profit.

The boundary between the SCC and the Fee may not be appropriate for all contracts. However, it has been drawn deliberately in order to be clear. To move the boundary for a particular contract requires a deduction or addition to the SCC. If this is being considered, reference to CIRIA Report 85 is recommended.

The following list gives some examples of cost components not included in the SCC. It is not exhaustive and therefore does not form a schedule of the Fee.

- Head office charges and overheads (unless specified for design, manufacture or fabrication through the overhead percentages).
- Insurance premiums – including, for example, employer's liability insurance for the *Contractor*'s staff and labour.
- Corporation tax.
- Advertising and recruitment costs.
- Sureties and guarantees required for the contract including 'fidelity bonds' required for employees who handle large sums of money which may be the *Employer*'s money, especially on a reimbursable contract.
- Some indirect payments to staff, especially on overseas contracts, for example, school fees. There is no principle involved here, only administrative convenience, recognising that contractors have different policies towards the payment of such items.

The *Contractor*'s profit is also excluded from the SCC and must therefore be allowed for in the Fee.

NOTES ON THE SHORTER SCC

Purpose and use

The Shorter SCC will always be used for the assessment of compensation events under Options A and B. Under certain circumstances (Clause 63.15) it may be used for the assessment of compensation events under Options C, D and E.

Main differences from full SCC

The Shorter SCC has been developed from the full SCC and many of the explanatory notes and principles for the full SCC will apply to the Shorter SCC. The following notes explain the main differences between the two schedules.

People 1

The first two bullet points are identical to the full SCC but a third one has been added, drawing in text from item 14 of the full SCC. This enables item 11 of the Shorter SCC to require the *Contractor* to justify only the amounts paid for people, which simplifies the process.

The intention is that amounts paid in the Shorter SCC would cover all the specific items listed in the full SCC. It is recommended that the *Project Manager* and *Contractor* agree early in the contract how these amounts are to be built up.

Equipment 2

As with the full SCC, all accommodation is treated as Equipment.

The cost components for Equipment in the Shorter SCC make use of published lists and rates, such as the 'CECA Schedule of Dayworks carried out incidental to contract works', published in the United Kingdom. Items of Equipment likely to be used, but which are not included in a particular published list, can be listed separately in part two of the Contract Data when the *Contractor* submits his tender.

As the definition of Equipment includes scaffolding, temporary sheet piling etc., tenderers should ensure that rates for these are included in item 22 of the Shorter SCC if they are likely to represent a significant cost and are not included in the published lists referred to in item 21. A possible alternative is for the tenderer to allow for their costs in the percentage for people overheads, but this would incur some risk.

Occasionally Equipment may be required as a result of a compensation event which is not in the published list and not listed in the Contract Data. This is covered by item 27, using either competitively tendered or open market rates.

The Equipment rates stated in the published lists will require adjustment by the 'percentage adjustment for listed Equipment' referred to in item 21 and tendered in part two of the Contract Data. This adjustment is required because, for example, the rates in the FCEC Schedule of Dayworks includes an element for overheads and profit. In the ECC, these are included in the Fee. Hence the rates should be adjusted downwards. Also, in some cases the published rates may not be appropriate to local circumstances, and may need adjusting upwards or downwards.

A combination of these and other relevant factors will need to be taken into account to produce the particular percentage adjustment required.

Plant and Materials 3

See notes for the full SCC as the clauses are identical in both schedules.

Charges 4

In the Shorter SCC a percentage is applied to the total cost of people (item 11). Such a procedure is adopted to ease the calculation of payments to Others. The percentage for people overheads, therefore, using the Shorter SCC covers the charges as listed. The percentage for Working Areas overheads is not used with the Shorter SCC.

Note that under the third bullet of 41, whilst accommodation itself is treated as Equipment, supplies and services for accommodation are covered by the percentage for people overheads. However, the word 'services' does not include the services of people as they can only be included in one cost component, which will be People.

Manufacturing and fabrication	5	Under Options A and B the Shorter SCC applies to both the *Contractor*'s costs and Subcontractor's costs. The *Contractor* cannot predict, at tender stage, whether a compensation event requiring manufacturing and fabrication outsider the Working Areas will affect a particular Subcontractor or affect their own fabrication shop. Consequently the cost component is amounts paid by the *Contractor*, which is also administratively simpler than the approach adopted in the full SCC.
Design and insurance	6 and 7	See notes for the full SCC as the clauses are identical in both schedules.

Engineering and Construction Subcontract

For this section of the guidance notes the word Subcontractor is printed in italics if it is used in reference to the NEC Engineering and Construction Subcontract (ECS). The ECS is based on the ECC in order to achieve identical working for similar contract situations. The reason for this is that the relationship between the *Contractor* and the *Subcontractor* is similar to that between the *Employer* and *Contractor*. There are, however, certain additions and amendments required in the subcontract which arise from the main contract.

The ECC includes (amongst others) the following parties

- the *Employer*
- the *Project Manager*, and
- the *Supervisor*.

The ECS equivalents have been combined into one (the *Contractor*) as it was considered that, while different people in the *Contractor*'s organisation may perform the separate functions, it would be too complicated to have different legal persons for each separate subcontract. This has required some amendments where the ECC text describes actions by the *Employer*, *Project Manager* and *Supervisor*.

All the ECC Options have been retained for the subcontract except Option F. Thus, for example, the main contract may be a priced contract with a bill of quantities, and the subcontract may be based on an activity schedule, or on a cost reimbursement option.

To avoid confusion, the following items have been prefixed 'subcontract'

- *works*,
- *starting date*,
- Completion Date, and
- Works Information.

Other changes are

- Subsubcontractor for Subcontractor,
- Subcontract Data for Contract Data,
- ECC is referred to as the main contract.

The main additions and amendments arising from provisions of the main contract are described below.

Subcontract documents

In preparing the subcontract the *Contractor* must be precise in detailing the documentation which comprises both the Subcontract Works Information and the subcontract Site Information. It is not sufficient for the *Contractor* to merely generalise by, for example, stating 'The Main Contract Works Information and Site Information shall be incorporated into this subcontract'. A properly drafted subcontract must state what these documents are, especially if the *Contractor* decides upon a different main Option for the subcontract to that under the main contract.

It is recommended that the *Contractor* chooses a main Option for the subcontract consistent with that of the main contract. However, in some circumstances the *Contractor* will engage a subcontractor under a different main Option: for example, where the *Subcontractor* is offering a lump sum price (Option A) but the *Contractor* is under an Option B contract.

It is usual for the Subcontract Works Information to be based upon and comprise documentation such as specification and drawings. Similarly, subcontract Site Information will most probably be that from the main contract but might be added to by the *Contractor* if, for example, he has carried out further site investigation work prior to seeking to sublet a part of the *works*.

Hence where the *Contractor* is incorporating main contract data into a subcontract, precise schedules should be prepared and expressly identified in the Subcontract Data part one.

It may be desirable for the *Subcontractor* to have a knowledge of the full general main contract documentation so that he has notice of them. In this case the *Subcontractor* should be given a copy or, as is more usual, he may inspect them and extract copies of any relevant parts. Either way it is recommended that the general main contract documentation or the relevant parts of it is incorporated in the subcontract by reference in the Subcontract Data.

Because of the inevitable difference in obligations between the main contract and subcontract there are some special considerations which the parties to the subcontract should be aware of.

Disputes

A provision has been included to cater for a dispute arising under the main contract which concerns the *subcontract works*. This enables the *Contractor* to require that such a dispute can be dealt with jointly with the dispute under the main contract by the main contract *Adjudicator*. This avoids two different adjudicators making different decisions on the same dispute.

The subcontract *Adjudicator* may be a person different from the main contract *Adjudicator*. His function is to deal with disputes which arise only between the *Contractor* and *Subcontractor* and which do not concern the *Employer*.

If any of the three parties to a joint dispute disagrees with the *Adjudicator*'s decision, he may refer it to the *tribunal*, as in the case of a dispute between only two contracting parties.

Termination

If the main contract is terminated, the *Contractor* will wish to terminate the subcontracts. The payment consequences depend upon whether the termination is due to the *Subcontractor*'s default or not.

Time periods

Time periods stated in the ECS have been adjusted to allow for associated actions under the main contract. Time limits in the subcontract for sending information to the *Contractor* are less than the times stated in the main contract for sending information to the *Project Manager* in order to allow time for the *Contractor* to incorporate or process the information. Time limits in the subcontract for transmitting decisions or payments to the *Subcontractor* are greater than the equivalent times stated in the main contract, for similar reasons.

Some time periods are not stated in the ECS but, like the main contract, are to be inserted in the Subcontract Data. Examples are a reply to a communication or the submission of a revised programme.

The *Contractor* must ensure that the time periods in the Subcontract Data are adequate for proper reply but not excessive so as to prevent the *Contractor* from sending a similar reply under the main contract.

Design Defects

It may be that, as part of his *subcontract works*, the *Subcontractor* is carrying all of the *Contractor*'s design obligation, or possibly only a small portion of it. Whatever obligation is passed to the *Subcontractor* should be reflected in the limit of the *Subcontractor*'s liability for design Defects entered in part one of the Subcontract Data.

Risks and insurance

The *Employer*'s risks remain, and the *Contractor* passes those of his risks under the main contract to the *Subcontractor* where they apply to the *subcontract works*. Double insurance is largely avoided since the insurance premiums payable by the *Contractor* under the main contract will reflect the proportion of the *works* which are subcontracted.

Under the ECS the risks carried by the *Contractor* for the works subcontracted are passed to the *Subcontractor* for the period from the *subcontract starting date* until the subcontract Defects Certificate has been issued. Outside of this period, with the exception of continuing liabilities, the *Contractor* or *Employer* (depending upon other main contract criteria) carries the risk for the *subcontract works*. Thus if the *subcontract completion date* and *defects date* are earlier than those of the main contract then the *Contractor* must recognise two important factors.

- The *Contractor* will carry the risk of and should ensure that his insurance cover is continuing for the *subcontract works*.
- The *Contractor* will carry the risk of Defects in the *subcontract works* from the conclusion of the *Subcontractor*'s liability for correcting his Defects upon the issue of the subcontract Defects Certificate.

Should it be important, for example, that the *Subcontractor* continues to correct Defects right up to Completion of the whole of the *works* (or even to the issue of the main contract Defects Certificate) then the Subcontract Data part one must properly reflect and include this intention of the Parties by incorporating appropriate *subcontract completion date* and *defects date*.

Notwithstanding the subcontract insurance provisions, the *Contractor* still carries responsibility for the performance of the *Subcontractor* in the ECC and the *Subcontractor* is always responsible for insuring his own Equipment and his employees.

Delay damages

When considering delay damages under Options X5 and X6 it is not sufficient for the *Contractor* to insert in the Subcontract Data optional statements general wording such as 'delay damages as main contract'. The damages must be a genuine pre-estimate at the time when the subcontract is made of the likely losses that the *Contractor* will suffer if there is a delay by the *Subcontractor*.

If the *subcontract works* are critical or the *subcontract completion date* is coincidental with that of the main contract then it may be that the delay damages under the subcontract will be as those for the main contract. In circumstances where the subcontract is not critical or concerns only minor works, the delay damages must reflect this on the basis of a genuine pre-estimate of the loss the *Contractor* would suffer.

Guidance notes

Detailed guidance notes for the ECS have not been prepared since the principles can be understood from the ECC guidance notes.

Flow charts

Flow charts for the subcontract have not been prepared since the logic of the procedures can be understood from the ECC flow charts.

APPENDIX 1

Clause numbering system

Core and main Options

1 General

Core			Options			
Cl. no.	Title	Para. no.	Cl. no.	Title	Para. no.	Applicable options
10	Actions	10.1				
11	Identified and defined terms	11.1 11.2 (1) to (19)				
				Activity Schedule	11.2(20)	A, C
				Bill of Quantities	11.2(21)	B, D
				Defined Cost	11.2(22)	A, B
				Defined Cost	11.2(23)	C, D, E
				Defined Cost	11.2(24)	F
				Disallowed Cost	11.2(25)	C, D, E
				Disallowed Cost	11.2(26)	F
				Price for Work Done to Date	11.2(27)	A
				Price for Work Done to Date	11.2(28)	B
				Price for Work Done to Date	11.2(29)	C, D, E, F
				Prices	11.2(30)	A, C
				Prices	11.2(31)	B, D
				Prices	11.2(32)	E, F
				Total of the Prices	11.2(33)	D
12	Interpretation and the law	12.1 to 12.4				
13	Communications	13.1 to 13.8				
14	The *Project Manager* and the *Supervisor*	14.1 to 14.4				
15	Adding to the Working Areas	15.1				
16	Early warning	16.1 to 16.4				
17	Ambiguities and inconsistencies	17.1				
18	Illegal and impossible requirements	18.1				
19	Prevention	19.1				

2 The *Contractor*'s main responsibilities

	Core			Options		
Cl. no.	Title	Para. no.	Cl. no.	Title	Para. no.	Applicable Options
20	Providing the Works	20.1			20.2 20.3 20.4 20.5	F C, D, E, F C, D, E, F F
21	The *Contractor*'s design	21.1 to 21.3				
22	Using the *Contractor*'s design	22.1				
23	Design of Equipment	23.1				
24	People	24.1 24.2				
25	Working with the *Employer* and Others	25.1 to 25.3			26.4	C, D, E, F
26	Subcontracting	26.1 to 26.3				
27	Other responsibilities	27.1 to 27.4				

3 Time

	Core			Options		
Cl. no.	Title	Para. no.	Cl. no.	Title	Para. no.	Applicable Options
30	Starting, Completion and Key Dates	30.1 to 30.3				
31	The programme	31.1 to 31.3			31.4	A, C
32	Revising the programme	32.1 32.2				
33	Access to and use of the Site	33.1				
34	Instructions to stop or not to start work	34.1				
35	Take over	35.1 to 35.3				
36	Acceleration	36.1 36.2			36.3 36.4	A, B, C, D E, F

4 Testing and Defects

Core			Options			
Cl. no.	Title	Para. no.	Cl. no.	Title	Para. no.	Applicable Options
40	Tests and inspections	40.1 to 40.6				
41	Testing and inspection before delivery	41.1			40.7	C, D, E
42	Searching for and notifying Defects	42.1 42.2				
43	Correcting Defects	43.1 to 43.4				
44	Accepting Defects	44.1 44.2				
45	Uncorrected Defects	45.1 45.2				

5 Payment

Core			Options			
Cl. no.	Title	Para. no.	Cl. no.	Title	Para. no.	Applicable Options
50	Assessing the amount due	50.1 to 50.5				
					50.6 50.7	C, D E, F
51	Payment	51.1 to 51.4				
52	Defined Cost	52.1				
					52.2 52.3	C, D, E, F C, D, E, F
			53	The *Contractor*'s share	53.1 to 53.4	C
					53.5 to 53.8	D
			54	The Activity Schedule	54.1 to 54.3	A, C
			55	The Bill of Quantities	55.1	B, D

6 Compensation events

CI. no.	Title	Para. no.	CI. no.	Title	Para. no.	Applicable Options
60	Compensation events	60.1(1) to (19) 60.2 60.3			60.4 to 60.7	B, D
61	Notifying compensation events	61.1 to 61.7				
62	Quotations for compensation events	62.1 to 62.6				
63	Assessing compensation events	63.1 to 63.9			63.10 63.11 63.12 63.13 63.14 63.15	A, B C, D A, C B, D A C, D, E
64	The Project Manager's assessments	64.1 to 64.4				
65	Implementing compensation events	65.1 65.2			65.3 65.4	E, F A, B, C, D

7 Title

CI. no.	Title	Para. no.	CI. no.	Title	Para. no.	Applicable Options
70	The Employer's title to Plant and Materials	70.1 70.2				
71	Marking Equipment, Plant and Materials outside the Working Areas	71.1				
72	Removing Equipment	72.1				
73	Objects and materials within the Site	73.1 73.2				

8 Risks and insurance

Core			Options			
Cl. no.	Title	Para. no.	Cl. no.	Title	Para. no.	Applicable Options
80	*Employer*'s risks	80.1				
81	The *Contractor*'s risks	81.1				
82	Repairs	82.1				
83	Indemnity	83.1 83.2				
84	Insurance cover	84.1 84.2				
85	Insurance policies	85.1 to 85.4				
86	If the *Contractor* does not insure	86.1				
87	Insurance by the *Employer*	87.1 to 87.3				

9 Termination

Core			Options			
Cl. no.	Title	Para. no.	Cl. no.	Title	Para. no.	Applicable Options
90	Termination	90.1 to 90.5				
91	Reasons for termination	91.1 to 91.7				
92	Procedures on termination	92.1 92.2				
93	Payment on termination	93.1 93.2			93.3 93.4 93.5 93.6	A C D C, D

Secondary Options

Option Ref.	Title	Clause. no.	Can be used with these main Options
DISPUTE RESOLUTION			
W1	Dispute Resolution	W1.1 to W1.4	A to F
W2	Dispute Resolution	W2.1 to W2.4	A to F
SECONDARY			
X1	Price adjustment for inflation	X1.1 to X1.5	A to D
X2	Changes in the law	X2.1	A to F
X3	Multiple currencies	X3.1 X3.2	A, B
X4	Parent company guarantee	X4.1	A to F
X5	Sectional Completion	X5.1	A to F
X6	Bonus for early Completion	X6.1	A to F
X7	Delay damages	X7.1 to X7.3	A to F
X8 to X11	Not used in ECC		A to F
X12	Partnering	X12.1 to X12.4	A to F
X13	Performance bond	X13.1	A to F
X14	Advanced payment to the *Contractor*	X14.1 to X14.3	A to F
X15	Limitation of the *Contractor*'s liability for his design to reasonable skill and care	X15.1 X15.2	A to F
X16	Retention	X16.1 X16.2	A to E
X17	Low performance damages	X17.1	A to F
X18	Limitation of liability	X18.1 to X18.5	
X19	Not used in ECC		
X20	Key Performance Indicators	X20.1 to X20.5	A to F
OPTIONS DEALING WITH NATIONAL LEGISLATION			
Y(UK)2	The Housing Grants, Construction and Regeneration Act 1996	Y2.1 to Y2.4	A to F
Y(UK)3	The Contracts (Rights of Third Parties) Act 1999	Y3.1	A to F
ADDITIONAL CONDITIONS			
Z1 etc.	*Additional conditions of contract* (as required for a specific contract)	Z1.1 etc.	A to F

APPENDIX 2

Sample form of tender

TENDER

The *works* ....

To .... (the *Employer*)

Address ....

....

....

....

We offer to Provide the Works in accordance with the Contract Data part one and the attached Contract Data part two for a sum to be determined in accordance with the *conditions of contract.*

You may accept this offer on or before [date of last day for acceptance]

Yours faithfully,

Signed ....

Name ....

Position ....

On behalf of .... (the *Contractor*)

Address ....

....

....

....

Date ....

APPENDIX 3

Sample form of agreement

This agreement is made on the . . . . day of . . . . 20 . . . . . between

• . . . .

of . . . .

. . . . (the *Employer*) and

• . . . .

of . . . .

. . . . (the *Contractor*)

The *Employer* wishes to have the following works provided

. . . .

. . . .

. . . .

1. The *Contractor* will Provide the Works in accordance with the *conditions of contract* identified in the Contract Data.

2. The *Employer* will pay the *Contractor* the amount due and carry out his duties in accordance with the *conditions of contract* identified in the Contract Data.

3. The documents forming part of this agreement are

   • the *Contractor*'s tender
   • the *Employer*'s letter of acceptance
   • the Contract Data part one
   • the Contract Data part two
   • the following documents

. . . .

. . . .

. . . .

. . . .

Signed by

Name . . . .

Position . . . .

On behalf of (*Employer*)

. . . .

and

Signed by

Name. . . . .

Position . . . .

On behalf of (*Contractor*)

. . . .

ALTERNATIVE IF AGREEMENT IF EXECUTED AS A DEED UNDER ENGLISH LAW AND BOTH *EMPLOYER* AND *CONTRACTOR* ARE COMPANIES

• Executed as a deed by the *Employer*

or * by   (name of Director)

. . . .(signature of Director)

. . . .(name of Director or Company Secretary)

. . . . (signature of Director or Company Secretary)

• and as a deed by the *Contractor*

. . . .(name of Director)

. . . .(signature of Director)

. . . .(name of Director or Company Secretary)

. . . . (signature of Director or Company Secretary)

APPENDIX 4

Model tender assessment sheet (to be used only for Options A and B)

Introduction

Two categories of adjustment to the tendered total of the Prices are considered. The first relates only to those tenders where the tenderer has been asked to propose the Completion Date. The second covers the likely cost of changes resulting from compensation events.

Where the tenderer has been asked to propose the Completion Date, an adjustment should be made to reflect the value to the *Employer* of having the works completed as soon as possible. Ideally this is based on the delay damages stated in the Contract Data part one, but if delay damages are not used the *Employer* should make an assessment of the value of completion – or the cost of late completion, which should amount to the same thing.

Almost every contract will have some compensation events, resulting in an outturn cost higher than the tendered total of the Prices. This assessment assumes that the cost of most of the basic resources involved in compensation events will be the same for all tenderers and so only examines elements where there will be differences.

The *Employer* must first make an estimate of the likely difference between tender and outturn prices; this will vary depending on various factors such as the nature of the work to be carried out, the nature of the site and the degree of site investigation work carried out. The difference is expressed as a percentage of the tendered total of the Prices.

This difference must then be subdivided into cost elements – people, Equipment, Subcontractors, design and the *Contractor*'s Fee. Note that design may be required for temporary works even if the *Contractor* is not responsible for the design of any of the *works*.

Note that the two elements making up the Fee (the *direct fee percentage* and the *subcontracted fee percentage*) are applied to different parts of the adjustments.

The figure derived from these adjustments is *not* an estimate of the final outturn cost as it only takes into account those elements which will differ between tenderers.

In the example that follows, the following figures will be used to illustrate the procedure.

	Ref.		Source
Tendered total of the Prices	A	£1,320,800	Contract Data part two
Tendered *completion date*	B	36 weeks after the *starting date*	Contract Data part two
Employer's estimate of earliest practical *completion date*	C	32 weeks after the *starting date*	*Employer*'s estimate
Delay damages for the whole of the *works* (Option X7)	D	£4,300/week	Contract Data part one
Weighted average of the cost of design staff	E	£48/hour	Contract Data part two
Design overhead	F	35%	Contract Data part two

	Ref.		Source
Direct fee percentage	G	11%	Contract Data part two
Difference between tender and outturn cost (excluding percentage additions)	H	12%	*Employer*'s estimate
People element of this increase	J	25%	*Employer*'s estimate
People overheads	K	45%	Contract Data part two
Equipment element of increase	L	35%	Employers estimate
Percentage for adjustment of Equipment in the published list	M	−10%	Contract Data part two
Subcontract element of increase	N	25%	*Employer*'s estimate
Subcontracted fee percentage	P	8%	Contract Data part two
Design time required	Q	25 hours	*Employer*'s estimate

Adjustment sheet – example

1	Time adjustment (if required)	$(B - C) \times D$	$(36 - 32) \times £4{,}300$		£17,200
2	Charges for people overheads	$A \times H \times J \times K$	$£1{,}320{,}800 \times 12\% \times 25\% \times 45\%$		£17,830
3	Equipment	$A \times H \times L \times M$	$£1{,}320{,}800 \times 12\% \times 35\% \times (-10\%)$		−£5,547
4	Design cost	$Q \times E$	25×48		£1,200
5	Design overheads	Design cost $\times$ F	$£1{,}200 \times 35\%$		£420
6	Fee:				
	Fee on additional direct cost	$A \times (100 - N) \times H \times G$	$£1{,}320{,}800 \times 75\% \times 12\% \times 11\%$ $11\% \times (£17{,}830 + £1{,}200 + £420)$	£13,076	
	Fee on additional subcontracted work	$A \times N \times H \times P$	$£1{,}320{,}800 \times 25\% \times 12\% \times 8\%$	£3,170	
	Total Fee			£16,246	£16,246
	Total adjustment				£47,349
	Tendered total of the Prices (A)				£1,320,800
	Notional total for assessment purposes				**£1,368,149**

APPENDIX 5

Contract Data – worked example

Introduction

The following pages show the Contract Data completed for a fictitious contract. The purpose of this example is to help those unfamiliar with the NEC system to complete the tender documents. It should be read in conjunction with the notes included under the chapter 'Tender Documents'.

The following points should be noted.

- The ECC text of the Contract Data formats is reproduced as printed, together with the explanatory sentences which are in bold type. The explanatory sentences (e.g. 'Statements given in all contracts' and sentences beginning 'If...') are only for the guidance of users and should not be reproduced on an actual Contract Data.

- For clarity, quantities have been inserted in the appropriate places. **The figures given are imaginary and should not be taken as typical and certainly do not have the status of 'recommended by the NEC Panel'.** The examples of entries are not necessarily consistent throughout.

- Most optional statements have been completed so that users can see what should be written if that Option is chosen. **In a real enquiry only those statements relevant to the Options chosen should be completed.**

- If an optional statement is required it should be inserted in an appropriate position in the actual Contract Data, within the statements for the relevant section of the ECC.

- **The statements in the boxes only provide a very abbreviated commentary on completing the Contract Data and should not be relied on.** Reference must be made to the conditions themselves and to the relevant guidance notes for a fuller treatment of topics.

- **The *Employer* must decide actual details based on the nature of the contract and the allocation of risk required.**

- **Those drawing up tender documents are advised to take care when completing the Contract Data that excessive risks are not passed to the *Contractor*.** The ECC system is much more flexible than any other published contract and allows a wide range of *Employer*'s choice of allocation of risks on the *Contractor*, which would be limited in other documents. **Common sense needs to be applied otherwise bids will reflect the unrealistic aspirations of the *Employer*.** In particular combinations including tight programmes, extended defects dates, large bonds, fixed prices, large retentions and heavy damages should only be used if the *Employer*'s key strategy demands them.

- **The words of the ECC Contract Data formats should be reproduced without change.** Users of the ECC are granted a limited licence by the Institution of Civil Engineers to reproduce the text in tenders solely for the purpose of inviting, assessing and managing contracts.

Part one – Data provided by the *Employer*

Completion of the data in full, according to the Options chosen, is essential to create a complete contract.

Statements given in all contracts

1 General

- The *conditions of contract* are the core clauses and the clauses for main Option **A**, dispute resolution Option **W1** and secondary Options **X3, X4, X7, X13, X16, Y(UK)2, Y(UK)3 and Z** of the NEC3 Engineering and Construction Contract June 2005 (with amendments June 2006).

  > Choose one main Option (A to F) and one dispute resolution Option (W1 or W2). In addition choose any of the secondary Options appropriate to the chosen contract strategy, ensuring that these are compatible with the chosen main Option.

- The *works* are **the construction of the Much Binding bypass, including the design of the bridge crossing the River Binding.**

  > Describe the *works* clearly but briefly. The description should enable the *works* to be identified but should not go into details; details will be included in the Works Information. It may be helpful to include the location of the *works* if this is not clear from the description.
  >
  > It is sensible to use a shorter title in correspondence – in this case, for example, 'The Much Binding Bypass' would be an obvious choice.

- The *Employer* is

  > The *Employer*'s legal name and usual address are given here. The address need not be the registered office unless the applicable law so requires.

  Name **Greenwheat County Council**

  Address **County Hall**
  Greater Binding
  Greenwheatshire
  GN7 3BB.

- The *Project Manager* is

  > It is essential that the person chosen as *Project Manager* is sufficiently close to the work and have the time to carry out his duties effectively. He must also have sufficient authority to exercise the authority given to him under the contract.
  >
  > See the guidance notes (GNs) on the *Project Manager*.

  Name **Mr K Williams**

  Address **County Hall**
  Greater Binding
  Greenwheatshire
  GN7 3BB.

- The *Supervisor* is

  Name **Mr H Paddick**

  Address **County Hall**
  Greater Binding
  Greenwheatshire
  GN7 3BB.

  > The *Supervisor*'s role is essentially to check that the works are constructed in accordance with the drawings and specification.
  >
  > If there is manufacture off site, the *Supervisor* may be represented by, for example, resident inspectors to whom he would delegate powers under Clause 14.2.
  >
  > The *Supervisor* does have the vital responsibility of issuing the Defects Certificate – see Clause 43.2.

- The *Adjudicator* is

  > The *Adjudicator* proposed by the *Employer* can be named here, or a list of suggested names could be proposed, here or in the Instructions to Tenderers. The most important aspect is that the *Adjudicator* must be acceptable to both parties.

  Name **Mr I Judge**

  Address **Test House**
  Michelmersh
  Hampshire.

- The Works Information is in **Parts 2, 3 and 4 of the enquiry document.**

- The Site Information is in **Part 5 of the enquiry document.**

- The *boundaries of the site* are **shown on drawing SP/104 Revision C.**

  > It is generally easier to show the *boundaries of the site* on a drawing than to define them in words.

- The *language of this contract* is **English.**

It is possible for the law of one country to be applied in the courts of another. Thus the place of jurisdiction should be stated here as well as the law that is to apply to the contract.

- The *law of the contract* is the law of **England and Wales, subject to the jurisdiction of the courts of England and Wales.**

- The *period for reply* is **2 weeks.**

- The *Adjudicator nominating body* is **the Institution of Civil Engineers**

The period for reply (see GNs on Clause 13) must be sufficient for the parties to respond, but should be sufficiently brief to maintain the principle of dealing with problems before they arise.

Care should be taken when choosing the Ajudicator – see notes on Dispute Resolution options for their relevant experience, qualifications and ability.

The Institution of Civil Engineers maintains a list of suitably qualified and experienced people to act as adjudicators. Several other institutions maintain similar lists.

The choice is usually between arbitration and litigation

- The *tribunal* is **arbitration.**

- The following matters will be included in the Risk Register
  The risk that the level of the River Binding exceeds 2.6 m as measured at the weir at Little Binding.

The *Employer* lists here the risks that he requires to be included in the Risk Register. This alerts the tenderer to the risks, and encourages the *Project Manager* and the *Contractor* to discuss how best to avoid or minimise their effects.

3 Time

- The *starting date* is **3 October 2005.**

- The *access dates* are

Part of the Site	Date
1 **All areas west of the River Binding**	**3 October 2005**
2 **Remainder of the Site**	**31 October 2005.**

- The *Contractor* submits revised programmes at intervals no longer than **5** weeks.

Making the period five weeks maximum allows for a 'normal' site administration procedure, which is to have monthly revisions of a programme.

4 Testing and Defects

- The *defects date* is **52** weeks after Completion of the whole of the *works*.

- The *defect correction period* is **3** weeks except that

  - The *defect correction period* for **Plant in the School Underpass is 12** weeks.

This is the period within which the *Contractor* is liable to correct Defects.

In some circumstances it may be sensible to have different defects dates for different parts of the works – soft landscaping is a typical example – but unnecessary complication should be avoided.

There is little point in having an unreasonably short *defect correction period*. It makes for inefficient working on the part of the *Contractor*.

The *Employer* might require shorter periods for Defects that prevent his using the *works* and/or allow longer periods for parts of the *works* that require dismantling and repair or replacement if they are faulty.

5 Payment

- The *currency of this contract* is the **pound sterling.**

- The *assessment interval* is **5** weeks (not more than five).

- The *interest rate* is **2.5** % per annum (not less than 2) above the **base rate in force from time to time of the Bank of England.**

The limit of five weeks is to ensure a reasonable cash flow for the *Contractor*. In practice most payment procedures will be based on calendar months.

The inter bank lending rates of the UK 'high street' banks are sometimes used, but they effectively shadow the Bank of England's base rate.

If the contract is overseas, the *Employer* should select a bank to reflect the currency of the contract, not necessarily the country where the works are being carried out.

6 Compensation events
- The place where weather is to be recorded is

  Lyneham, Wiltshire.

  See GN on Clause 60.1(13).

- The *weather measurements* to be recorded for each calendar month are

  See GN on Clause 60.1(13).

  - the cumulative rainfall (mm)
  - the number of days with rainfall more than 5 mm
  - the number of days with minimum air temperature less than 0 degrees Celsius
  - the number of days with snow lying at **09:00** hours GMT
  - and these measurements:

  It is important not to add *weather measurements* that cannot be readily and regularly recorded. Only the larger sites are likely to install their own weather station. Additional weather measurements should suit the risks associated with the works. For example, for a project dependent upon tower cranes it may be appropriate to include the number of days that winds exceeded the maximum wind speeds at which the cranes can work.

- The *weather measurements* are supplied by
  The Met Office, Building Consultancy Group, Johnson House, London Road, Bracknell, Berkshire, RG12 2SY.

- The *weather data* are the records of past *weather measurements* for each calendar month which were recorded at **Lyneham, Wiltshire** and which are available from **The Met Office.**

  For consistency it is generally an advantage to have the *weather data* and *weather measurements* recorded at the same place in most circumstances.

  Where no recorded data are available

- Assumed values for the ten year return *weather data* for each *weather measurement* for each calendar month are
  stated as part of the Site Information in Part 5 of the enquiry document.

  This section is only used if there are no suitable *weather data* – for example when there is no available weather station.

8 Risks and insurance
- The minimum limit of indemnity for insurance in respect of loss of or damage to property (except the *works*, Plant and Materials and Equipment) and liability for bodily injury to or death of a person (not an employee of the *Contractor*) caused by activity in connection with this contract for any one event is **£2,000,000 (two million pounds).**

- The minimum limit of indemnity for insurance in respect of death of or bodily injury to employees of the *Contractor* arising out of and in the course of their employment in connection with this contract for any one event is **£10,000,000 (ten million pounds).**

  Unless the *Employer* has his own insurance department or access to insurance specialists, it is sensible to get advice on the figures to be inserted here.

  This will be especially true when working outside the UK.

Optional statements

If the *tribunal* is arbitration

See GN on Clause W1.4 or W2.4.

- The *arbitration procedure* **is the latest version of the Institution of Civil Engineers Arbitration Procedure or any amendment or modification to it in force when the arbitrator is appointed.**
- The place where arbitration is to be held is **London.**
- The person or organisation who will choose an arbitrator
  - if the Parties cannot agree a choice or
  - if the *arbitration procedure* does not state who selects an arbitrator is
  The Institution of Civil Engineers.

If the *Employer* has decided the *completion date* for the whole of the *works*

See GN on Clause 30.

- The *completion date* for the whole of the *works* is **15 October 2007.**

If the *Employer* is not willing to take over the *works* before the Completion Date

- The *Employer* is not willing to take over the *works* before the Completion Date.

  See GN on Clause 35.2.

If no programme is identified in part two of the Contract Data

- The *Contractor* is to submit a first programme for acceptance within **4** weeks of the Contract Date.

  See GN on Clause 31.1.

If the *Employer* has identified work which is to meet a stated *condition* by a *key date*

See GN on Clause 30.3. This could also be dealt with by using Sectional Completion (X5).

- The *key dates* and *conditions* to be met are

condition to be met	key date
1 **Western Roundabout open to traffic**	**5 June 2006.**

If the period in which payments are made is not three weeks and Y(UK)2 is not used

- The period within which payments are made is **2** weeks.

See GN on Clause 51.1.

See GN on Clause 51.1.

If Y(UK)2 is used and the final date for payment is not 14 days after the date when payment is due

- The period for payment is...

If there are additional *Employer's* risks

- These are additional *Employer's* risks

    1 **Planning permission for the work in the vicinity of the school (marked 'C' on drawing SP/104 Revision C) is not obtained by 10 October 2005.**

It may not be economical for the *Contractor* to assume a particular risk, especially a risk that has a low probability of occurrence but a very serious consequence.

If the *Employer* is to provide Plant and Materials

- The insurance against loss of or damage to the *works*, Plant and Materials is to include cover for Plant and Materials provided by the *Employer* for an amount of **£25,000.**

Insert the value or replacement cost of any 'free issue' Plant or Materials to be incorporated in the *works*.

If the *Employer* is to provide any of the insurances stated in the Insurance Table

- The *Employer* provides these insurances from the Insurance Table

    1 Insurance against **Loss of or damage to the *works*, Plant and Materials**

    Cover/indemnity is **£6,000,000**

    The deductibles are **£40,000.**

If the *Employer* has decided to provide any of the insurances, details should be entered here.

See GN on Clause 87.1.

If additional insurances are to be provided

- The *Employer* provides these additional insurances

    1 Insurance against..

    Cover/indemnity is..

    The deductibles are..

State any additional insurances to be provided by the *Employer*. This may include single site policies and other special arrangements.

See GN on Section 8.

- The *Contractor* provides these additional insurances

    1 Insurance against **faults in design (Professional Indemnity Insurance)**

    Cover/indemnity is **£2,000,000.**

If Option B or D is used

The edition used should also be stated.

- The *method of measurement* is **the Civil Engineering Method of Measurement third edition**

    amended as follows **no amendments**

    ....

If Option C or D is used

- The *Contractor's share percentages* and the *share ranges* are

See GN on Clause 53 before completing this section.

share range				Contractor's share percentage
less than		**80** %		**15** %
from	**80** % to	**90** %		**30** %
from	**90** % to	**110** %		**50** %
greater than		**110** %		**20** %

© copyright nec 2005 **149**

If Option C, D or E is used

- The *Contractor* prepares forecasts of Defined Cost for the *works* at intervals no longer than **5** .... weeks.

See GN on Clause 50.6.

- The *exchange rates* are those published in **the Financial Times** on **24 August 2005.**

The frequency will in most cases coincide with the monthly cycle of assessments, monthly meetings, monthly reports etc., so a five week maximum is sensible.

If Option X1 is used

- The proportions used to calculate the Price Adjustment Factor are

0.25	linked to the index for	**Labour and supervision**
0.30		**Plant and road vehicles**
0.10		**Ready mixed concrete**
0.15		**Coated macadam and bituminous products**
0.05		**DERV fuel**
0.05		**Steel for reinforcement**
0.10	non-adjustable	

1.00

See GN on Option X1.

- The *base date* for indices is **1 August 2005.**

- The indices are those prepared by **the Department for Trade and Industry.**

If Option X3 is used

- The *Employer* will pay for the items or activities listed below in the currencies stated

items and activities	other currency	total maximum payment in the currency
Provision of pumps in underpass	**Euro**	**20,000 Euro.**

See GN on Option X3.

- The exchange rates are those published in **the Financial Times** on **24 August 2005.**

If Option X5 is used

- The *completion date* for each *section* of the *works* is

section	description	completion date
1	**Western Roundabout**	**5 June 2006.**

See GN on Option X5. This could also be dealt with by using a Key Date.

If Options X5 and X6 are used together

- The bonus for each *section* of the *works* is

section	description	amount per day
1	**Western Roundabout**	**£250.**

There is no point in giving a bonus for early Completion unless it has a definite value to the *Employer*. In this case a developer is prepared to pay for early access to his site.

If Options X5 and X7 are used together

- Delay damages for each *section* of the works are

section	description	amount per day
1	**Western Roundabout**	**£400.**

If Option X6 is used (but not if Option X5 is also used)

- The bonus for the whole of the *works* is .... per day.

If Option X7 is used (but not if Option X5 is also used)

- Delay damages for Completion of the whole of the *works* are **£950** per day.

See GN on Option X7.

If Option X12 is used

- The *Client* is

See GN on Option X12.

Name	Greenwheat County Council
Address	County Hall
	Greater Binding
	Greenwheatshire
	GN7 3BB.

- The *Client's objective* is

  to improve the environment of Much Binding for residents and visitors.

- The Partnering Information is in

  Part 6 of the enquiry document.

If Option X13 is used

See GN on Option X13.

- The amount of the performance bond is **£1,000,000.**

If Option X14 is used

- The amount of the advanced payment is **£75,000.**

See GN on Option X14.

- The *Contractor* repays the instalments in assessments starting not less than **20** weeks after the Contract Date.

- The instalments are **10% of the payment otherwise due.**

- An advanced payment bond **is not** required.

If Option X16 is used

See GN on Option X16.

- The *retention free amount* is **£250,000.**

- The *retention percentage* is **5%.**

If Option X17 is used

See GN on Option X17. If used these should be a genuine pre-estimate of the likely costs the *Employer* will incur.

- The amounts for low performance damages are

amount	performance level
....	for ....
....	for ....
....	for ....
....	for ....

If Option X18 is used

- The *Contractor*'s liability to the *Employer* for indirect or consequential loss is limited to **50% of the total of the Prices at the Contract Date.**

- For any one event, the *Contractor*'s liability to the *Employer* for loss of or damage to the *Employer*'s property is limited to **£150,000.**

- The *Contractor*'s liability for Defects due to his design which are not listed on the Defects Certificate is limited to **£250,000.**

See GN on Option X18.

- The *Contractor*'s total liability to the *Employer* for all matters arising under or in connection with this contract, other than excluded matters, is **unlimited.**

- The *end of liability date* is **10** years after the Completion of the whole of the *works*.

If Option X20 is used (but not if Option X12 is also used)

- The *incentive schedule* for Key Performance Indicators is in **Attachment 1 to this Contract Data.**

- A report of performance against each Key Performance Indicator is provided at intervals of **3** months.

If Option Y(UK)3 is used

See GN on Option Y(UK)3.

- term .... person or organisation

  Responsibility to remedy Defects .... **Highways Agency.**

If Option Z is used

- The *additional conditions of contract* are **set out in part 2 of the enquiry documents.**

The *additional conditions of contract* will become part of the contract, and so should be easily identified and logically located. Most people attach them to the Contract Data part one.

Part two – Data provided by the *Contractor*

Completion of the data in full, according to the Options chosen, is essential to create a complete contract.

Statements given in all contracts

• The *Contractor* is

Name	**Woodstone Construction Ltd**
Address	**Woodstone House**
	Collingbourne Bellinger
	Wincanton
	AB3 7TT.

> Full legal name of *Contractor*.

> Use the address from which the *Contractor* intends to manage the contract. This need not be the company's registered address.
>
> Include the postcode.

• The *direct fee percentage* is **10%**.

See GN on Clause 11.2(8).

• The *subcontracted fee percentage* is **7.5%**.

• The *working areas* are the Site and

Borrow pit adjacent to the new road at chainage 18 + 00 (see drawing WCL/Tend/002).

> These *working areas* should satisfy the criteria set out in Clause 15.1.
>
> See GNs on Clause 11.2(18) and 15.1.

> Frequently the *Employer* will have listed in the Instructions to Tenderers the jobs for which he wants to see key people nominated.
>
> See GN on Clause 24.

• The key people are

(1) Name **T Blair**

Job **Site Agent**

Responsibilities **Overall responsibility for the contract**

Qualifications **C.Eng, MICE**

Experience **15 years in civil engineering construction – see attached CV.**

(2) Name **A Campbell**

Job **Construction Manager**

Responsibilities **Control of all construction resources**

Qualifications **No formal qualifications**

Experience **20 years in civil engineering construction, 8 as General Foreman or Construction Manager – see attached CV.**

• The following matters will be included in the Risk Register

The risk that contaminated material is found within *the boundaries of the site*.

> See GN on Clauses 11.2(14) and (16).

> The *Employer* should insert the appropriate optional statements for completion by tenderers before issuing the enquiry documents.

Optional statements

If the *Contractor* is to provide Works Information for his design

• The Works Information for the *Contractor's* design is in

Section 4 of the Tender Submission, headed 'Design of the River Binding Bridge'.

> If the *Contractor* is required to carry out design of all or part of the *works* and to submit some details as part of his tender submission, his calculations and any drawings should be referenced here.

If a programme is to be identified in the Contract Data

• The programme identified in the Contract Data is

Programme reference WCL/Prog/T1.

If the *Contractor* is to decide the *completion date* for the whole of the *works*

• The *completion date* for the whole of the *works* is **1 October 2007.**

> This statement is used if the *Employer* wishes tenderers to offer a *completion date*. He should set out his requirements in the Instructions to Tenderers, and say how, if at all, different dates will be taken into account in assessing tenders.

If Option A or C is used

- The *activity schedule* is **Document reference WCL/AS/01.**

The *activity schedule* is normally prepared by the tenderer, with the *Employer* setting out 'rules' for how he wants it set out. Any such rules will be in the instructions to tenderers.

If Option B or D is used

- The *bill of quantities* is **Document reference WCL/BoQ/01.**

The *bill of quantities* will be drawn up by the *Employer* and filled in by the tenderer.

If Option A, B, C or D is used

- The tendered total of the Prices is **£5,800,785 (five million eight hundred thousand seven hundred and eighty five pounds sterling).**

If the *Employer* has asked tenderers to insert this figure in the Form of Tender there may be no need to repeat it here.

If Option F is used

- Work which the *Contractor* will do himself is ....

  activity   *price* (lump sum or unit rate)

See GN on Option F in Contract Strategy section.

If Option A or B is used

Data for the Shorter Schedule of Cost Components

- The percentage for people overheads is **45** %.

- The published list of Equipment is the last edition of the list published by **The Civil Engineering Contractors Association.**

- The percentage for adjustment for Equipment in the published list is **−20** % (state plus or minus).

- The rates for other Equipment are

Equipment	size or capacity	rate
Barge mounted backhoe	**1.5 m³ bucket**	**£180/hr.**

Include here any equipment that is not covered by the selected published list – such as dredgers or special cranes.

- The hourly rates for Defined Cost of design outside the Working Areas are

category of employee	hourly rate
Senior engineer	**£45**
Junior Engineer	**£32**
Draughtsperson	**£26**
Tracer	**£12.**

- The percentage for design overheads is **28** %.

- The categories of design employees whose travelling expenses to and from the Working Areas are included in Defined Cost are **all of the categories listed above.**

See GN on Shorter Schedule of Cost Components.

If Option C, D or E is used

Data for Schedule of Cost Components

- The listed items of Equipment purchased for work on this contract, with an on cost charge, are

Equipment	time-related charge	per time period
....	....	per ....
		per ....

See GN on Schedule of Cost Components.

- The rates for special Equipment are

Equipment	size or capacity	rate
....	....	

See GN on Schedule of Cost Components.

- The percentage for Working Areas overheads is **37.5** %.

See GN on Schedule of Cost Components. The percentage is applied to the direct cost of people; see the Schedule of Cost Components for a list of the items it is intended to cover.

- The hourly rates for Defined Cost of manufacture and fabrication outside the Working Areas are

category of employee	hourly rate
Skilled	**£22.50**
Semiskilled	**£19.50**
Unskilled	**£14.**

Include sufficient categories of employee to allow the cost to be identified readily.

Overhead costs should not be included.

- The percentage for manufacture and fabrication overheads is **225% at the Chepstow works, 260% at the Mendips works.**

It may be necessary to stipulate different percentages for different factories or different types of work.

Data for both schedules of cost components

- The hourly rates for Defined Cost of design outside the Working Areas are

category of employee	hourly rate
Senior Engineer	£45
Junior Engineer	£32
Draughtsperson	£26
Tracer	£12.

- The percentage for design overheads is **28** %.

- The categories of design employees whose travelling expenses to and from the Working Areas are included as a cost of design of the *works* and Equipment done outside the Working Areas are **all of the categories listed above.**

If Option C, D or E is used

Data for the Shorter Schedule of Cost Components

- The percentage for people overheads is **45** %.

- The published list of Equipment is the last edition of the list published by **The Civil Engineering Contractors Association.**

- The percentage for adjustment for Equipment in the published list is **–20** % (state plus or minus).

- The rates for other Equipment are

Equipment	size or capacity	rate